The Mighty Voice

BY MIRIAM GILBERT

Illustrated by Simon Jeruchim

The Mighty

COVENANT BOOKS

Jewish Publication Society

Voice/ISAIAH,

PROPHET AND POET

of America

Copyright © 1963 by the Jewish Publication Society of America
Library of Congress catalog card number 63-16055
First printing 1963
Manufactured in the United States of America
by The Haddon Craftsmen
Designed by Carrie Makover

Miriam Gilbert is also the author of:

Eli Whitney: Master Craftsman
I Wish I Were A Giraffee
Jane Addams: World Neighbor
Henry Ford: Maker of The Model T
Cross Country Adventure
Starting An Aquarium

She received the 1962 Brotherhood Award from the National Conference of Christians and Jews for the "Best Magazine Fiction Of the Year."

The Mighty Voice

"Here's your lost lamb" Isaiah said.

Chapter 1/

The bright April sun shimmered down, baking the brown limestone hills of Judah to new hardness. Isaiah scrambled up the rough path, which was now beginning to come alive with the first spring flowers.

"Wait, wait," Amoz, his father, called, panting. He signaled to him to stop. "Let's sit for a minute in the shade of this palm tree."

Isaiah paced back and forth impatiently, while his father rested. "Aren't you curious why King Uzziah has asked you to come?" he prodded.

"Jotham is the king," Amoz reminded him. "I go to visit him now as an uncle of Uzziah's."

Isaiah dropped down on the ground beside his father and tucked his long, straight legs under him. "Uzziah was a great king," he said slowly. "Even now, after all these years, the soldiers tell how he conquered the Philistines and the

Ammonites. Just the other day, a caravan, loaded with the most wondrous things, came in from Elath. If it hadn't been for Uzziah—"

Amoz pulled at his gray beard. Yes, the Red Sea port of Elath was a busy trading center, thanks to Uzziah's military victories. The paths the caravans took from the east and the south were safe at last. Spices, silks and jewels from all over the world flowed into Jerusalem.

"If it hadn't been for Uzziah—" Amoz stirred and his eyes traveled down the hill and across Jerusalem's flat-topped roofs. Away off in the haze stretched the Dead Sea and the road to Jericho. "If it hadn't been for Uzziah—there wouldn't be towers in the desert now to protect the trading ports. There wouldn't be cisterns and wells for the comfort of travelers along the way. If it hadn't been for Uzziah, Judah would never have enjoyed these many years of peace and prosperity."

"Some day," Isaiah's deep voice cut into Amoz's thoughts, "some day I will write a biography of King Uzziah, his acts first and last. I know that he was cursed with leprosy when he tried to take away the powers of Azariah, the chief priest of the Temple. But in spite of everything, some say that privately his deeds are greater than those of King Solomon."

Amoz lifted himself with a sigh. He steadied himself for a moment, leaning his bronzed hand against Isaiah's broad shoulder.

"Well, let's hear what Uzziah wishes of me now."

They continued the rest of the way up the hillside in silence. Suddenly in the midst of a grove of date and olive trees, they came upon a solitary dwelling set back from the rocky roadway.

Isaiah ran ahead eagerly. "Isaiah!" Amoz cried out like

the crack of a whip. "Don't you dare approach that house unless you are invited to enter."

Then from inside the doorway, which was covered by a heavy, richly embroidered purple curtain, they heard the voice of Uzziah. "Let the boy come in, Amoz. He can sit in a corner of the room. I have my own dark corner to hide my face and my grief."

Amoz drew aside the curtain. He started forward as if to embrace Uzziah, then stepped back. The King beckoned and Amoz and Isaiah sat on two small stools which were at the far side of the gloomy room. "I would not have troubled you, Amoz, but you were always my guide," Uzziah said. "I have had much time to reflect on the past. Often I think of those days when I first ascended the throne." Uzziah turned towards Isaiah, but his face was blanketed by the shadows. "I was just a few years older than Isaiah is now."

"Yes," Amoz smiled reminiscently. "You had just turned sixteen."

"It was a difficult time for me, Amoz. You knew that better than most. When I needed men of honor and trust, you were by my side." He drew his robe closer about his wasted body. "But it's not the past that has made me call you here."

"Things are well at court," Amoz hastened to assure him. "Jotham has taken over easily in your stead." Amoz hesitated. "You provided a good example for him. Now all he has to do is follow in the path of righteousness."

"Has he made peace with the priests? Tell me the truth, Amoz?"

"He's built a new gate in the Temple court," Isaiah burst

out. "It's very beautiful. The priests are well satisfied. Uriah says—"

"Isaiah, keep your peace," his father said sternly.

"Let the boy speak," Uzziah encouraged. "I don't hear many young voices these days and one day his voice will be mighty, loud and strong in our country. The courtiers are pleased with his sharp wit." Uzziah turned his yellowish eyes upon the boy. "I am depending on you for many great things, Isaiah, just as I have depended on your father." He paused. "I hear that Tiglath-Pileser II is going to be crowned at Nineveh."

"Yes," Amoz said.

Isaiah leaned forward, excitedly. How strange that this man, confined to a leper house, should be concerned that there would be a new king of Assyria. Isaiah had heard rumors at Court that Tiglath-Pileser was a ruthless, ambitious man, with designs for world power. But Assyria was a long way off.

"I hear that there is much unrest in Israel now that Jeroboam II has died." Uzziah smiled wryly as he watched Isaiah. "Does it surprise you that news trickles into my prison house?" Uzziah turned his attention back to Amoz. "Jotham is new at affairs of state. I have burdened him enough already. And I know that he's not well."

"But—" Amoz started to protest.

Uzziah held up his scaly hand. "Don't bring me words of comfort. Jotham was here not too many days ago. A father's eyes can see much." Uncomfortably, he shifted to one side. "We agreed that it would be necessary to send an ambassador to Tiglath-Pileser to find out his intentions towards Judah. We must assure him that we want peace. No one can fulfill this task better than you."

"There are others who can do the job as well," Amoz protested. "Eben or Yuval, for instance. Besides," he hesitated, "you know I have just finished mourning the loss of my wife. I wouldn't want to leave Isaiah alone at this time."

"For that very reason, it's important that you go. Nothing can ease sorrow as much as work. And take Isaiah along with you."

Isaiah stood up so quickly that he knocked over the stool. "Some day he will sit in the council of kings. It's not too soon for him to start traveling and learning the face of the world."

"Oh, Father, please," Isaiah pleaded.

"We'll see," Amoz said. "There's much to be done."

"It's already done," Uzziah said. "During the past few weeks, I've been making arrangements to pave the way for your journey. I didn't call you sooner because I didn't want to interfere with the Passover holiday."

"I knew something special was going to happen today," Isaiah burst out. "But I never expected anything like this. Early this morning I went to the farm of Enos, who grows the best barley in the valley. I wanted to get some sheaves to bring to the Temple. When I put my offering on the altar, I felt a hand touch my shoulder. I looked around," he paused, "and no one was near me."

"He's an impressionable boy, excited by the season," Amoz said apologetically. "The first breath of spring makes us all giddy."

"That's not all," Isaiah went on. "I gazed up at the two olivewood cherubim, which are over the sanctuary, and for a moment—just a fleeting instant—their dazzling gold wings fluttered." His husky voice seemed to cast a spell over Amoz and Uzziah so that now neither could speak. "I knew then," Isaiah's eyes smoldered, "that I had felt the hand of the Lord."

"You're a dreamer," Amoz said impatiently. "You should not think such things."

Isaiah felt hurt by his father's stinging words, and he stepped back as if he had been slapped. He looked appealingly at Uzziah but the old man seemed to have fallen into a drugged stupor. Isaiah wondered if perhaps he had said too much and ruined everything for them.

"I'm sorry," he faltered, when he saw Uzziah's head lower and a visible shudder pass through him.

Then Uzziah put out his withered hands and his voice was sick with anguish as he cried out, "If only I could put my hands on your shoulders and bless you." He turned to Amoz and there was a mist in his eyes. "You, I send out to do man's work, and you, Isaiah, you are to do the work of the Lord." He clapped his hands together and the sharp sound acted like a signal, breaking the spell that Isaiah had cast over the room. "I have ordered a gold chest, encrusted with many jewels, six silver wine goblets and many other royal presents for Tiglath-Pileser." Once more Uzziah was businesslike. "Jotham prepared official letters of state, giving you authority to talk in the name of the King. Only a small group of you will go. In that way, you will be able to make better time." He stood up and paced back and forth excitedly, caught up in the flush of his own words. "The asses and camels are gathered together. Jotham will give you two horses from the royal stable, one for you and one for Isaiah, to make your journey more comfortable. Your caravan will be ready to leave by the end of the week. You may take one of your menservants, if you wish, but I have arranged for a messenger and several other officials to go with you. Eben and Yuval are among them. Of course, you can add anyone whom you feel will help you accomplish your mission."

Amoz brushed away a tear. "You are still the King."

Uzziah bowed his head. "No, my son is King now. Don't forget that." Amoz recalled his own earlier rebuke to Isaiah. "I'm only acting as his servant, as you are." Uzziah put out his hand entreatingly, then dropped it. "There's one other thing, a private matter." His voice lowered. "The Babylonians are wise when it comes to medicine. By chance you may hear of a doctor who knows of some way to help Jotham—yes, even me. Perhaps some new combination of spices and herbs. I cannot stay here, hidden away, waiting for death, watching myself turn to dust." His proud shoulders drooped. "But no matter. May God bless you and your son." He turned and went into an inner room.

Amoz sat, unmoving, long after Uzziah had disappeared. Isaiah put out his hand and his father clasped it. They went out into the sunshine; the sudden light blinded them momentarily.

Isaiah breathed deeply. They were high up in the Judean hills now and Jerusalem stretched out below them. From this vantage point, Isaiah could see to the east the Mount of Olives and below the Valley of Jehoshaphat. How dry and desolate the earth looked from here; how deep and treacherous the ravines and gorges which slashed the hills. Yet each stone was dear to him. This was the land he loved.

"It's so quiet and beautiful up here; could I go exploring?" Isaiah asked.

His father hesitated. "All right, but don't forget yourself and stay past dark. You know how your aunt worries if you're late for dinner."

Isaiah eagerly scrambled up higher and higher, while his father descended by the way they had come.

Light-footed, sure-footed as a wild animal, Isaiah leaped across a dry gully. The stones were scorching, even through his sandals. He spotted the opening of one of the many caves; it seemed scooped out in the side of the hill as if by a child's hand. It looked cool and damp in the dark mouth of the cave and he stretched out, thinking back to Uzziah's talk. A shadow flickered across the front of the cave. Isaiah jumped up. Who could have followed him up here?

As Isaiah sprang to his feet, he heard the sound of rolling rocks, as if someone in flight had stumbled.

Isaiah circled behind the cave and there he saw Shebna, a boy about his own age.

"What are you doing here?"

"The same as you," Shebna snapped.

"You've been following my father and me, haven't you?" Isaiah accused. "Did you hear what King Uzziah said?"

"What if I did?" Shebna said.

"You don't have to go sneaking around for information," Isaiah said. "If you asked for it straight out, you'd get it sooner and better. Now that you know, isn't it wonderful that I'll be going to Nineveh with my father?"

"If you get there," Shebna said.

"What do you mean?"

"Nothing. But Tiglath-Pileser can't be trusted. None of the Assyrians can be trusted."

"We've got to give Tiglath-Pileser a chance to prove himself," Isaiah said. "I know how you feel because of your father—"

"Know how I feel?" Shebna spat. "My father was a Babylonian noble. He was a more important man in Babylon than your father is here. And then because he dared to fight the Assyrians, we had to flee, leaving everything behind, leaving our home like thieves in the night. Desperate, we came here to a strange land, a land of heathens—"

"Heathens!" Isaiah grabbed Shebna by the shoulders. "You are the heathen. You with your parade of many gods, one for this and one for that. We have one God, one only, and He is enough for us."

"We'll see about that when the time comes," Shebna said, his wiry body bending like a willow branch as he backed away from Isaiah. "And I warn you, it won't be long before the gods of Babylon will triumph." He touched the lapis lazuli amulet of the head of Pazuzu, which he wore around his neck.

"I'm sorry I lost my temper," Isaiah apologized. "I guess I'm just excited about the whole idea."

"I wish I were you," Shebna said. "But I would go with a different purpose in mind." He kicked savagely at a stone and sent it clattering down the hillside. "To my dying day, I'll do whatever I can to destroy the Assyrians." Shebna's piercing black eyes narrowed. "On his deathbed, I promised my father I would avenge his death on foreign soil."

Isaiah shrugged. "I suppose I can't blame you, but it would be wonderful if we didn't have to waste our lives, and the lives of others, with war. But how can I criticize you when my own people have not yet learned to walk in peace, in the ways of the God of Jacob?"

"You speak like a coward," Shebna taunted. "You've always tried to get out of a fight with words, instead of your fists."

Suddenly, they were startled to hear someone crying nearby. Isaiah looked about, curious. "It sounds like a baby, but that's impossible. How could a baby get up here?"

Isaiah whirled around at the sound of someone shouting

behind them. A tall boy with a shepherd's crook, wearing a rough goatskin cloak, came into view. "Hi," he called out to the two boys, "have either of you seen a baby lamb? It strayed from the herd."

"Oh, so that's what it is," Isaiah laughed. "The lamb must be somewhere around. We heard it bleating nearby. I know these hills well. I'll help you find it." He held out his hand to the boy. "You're strange around here, aren't you?"

The boy nodded. "I'm a Rechabite. We came to Jerusalem for the Passover festival. Our tents are pitched outside the city, but I thought I would take some of the sheep to graze up in the hills. They get restless when they're too confined."

"A Rechabite! A tent-dweller!" Shebna snorted. "How come you weren't afraid to venture into the city streets? Weren't you afraid you'd get eaten?"

The boy looked at Shebna in surprise. "We come here every Passover to go to the Temple. This year I sacrificed my pet lamb," he said proudly.

"Ha," Shebna said scornfully, "if you're not careful, maybe they'll sacrifice you next year."

The boy's face flushed. He stepped forward menacingly.

"Do not pay any attention to him," Isaiah intervened. "He's angry with me, not you. Come along with me up this path. The bleating sounds louder this way."

The young boy wavered. "I don't like to have fun made of the way my family and I live. We follow the traditions of Moses. We live a simple nomad life. I am not afraid of the city but of the evil in the city."

Isaiah nodded thoughtfully. "We are *a people laden with iniquity, who have forsaken the Lord.* Often when I have seen the feasting and carousing that goes on, even within the palace itself, I have wondered how we could have strayed so far from Moses' teachings."

"If you're going to sit around talking of your Moses, then I'm leaving," Shebna said.

"Don't mind him," Isaiah said. He bent down and crawled into the small opening of a cave on his stomach. In a moment, he came out with the baaing lamb.

"Here's your lost lamb," Isaiah said.

"Thank you," the boy said. "What's your name?"

"I am Isaiah, son of Amoz."

"I am Noam, son of Yael. We will be staying here a few more days, perhaps until the end of the week. Could you try to visit me? It gets lonely in the desert. In my tribe there are not many boys my age to talk to."

"I'll try," Isaiah promised. "I remember once when I was little, I threatened to run away from home and join the Rechabites." He broke off laughing. "My mother said it was the best thing that could happen to me." Isaiah waved. "Good-by, Noam. I hope to see you soon again."

At dawn, a royal guard called for Isaiah.

Chapter **2** /

In the few days that remained before the start of their journey, Isaiah was too busy to go to see the young Rechabite boy. He was pleased to catch a glimpse of him, hovering on the fringes of the crowd that had gathered at the city gates to bid them Godspeed.

Isaiah waved to Noam to come closer. The boy approached timidly, an older man at his side. "This is Yael, my father," Noam said. "I told him how you helped me. I wanted to say good-by to you before you left."

"Thank you," Isaiah said.

"If you ever need help at any time," Noam's father said, "you can call on us. We used to travel great distances, but now many of the nomad tribes are warring with one another. We will not be more than a day or two's journey from Jerusalem for our own safety."

Isaiah's friend, Eliakim, approached just then. "Your

father says everything is set. Chephren has already started off with the camels."

There was a high-pitched cry, and a breathless girl came running up to Yael and clung to him. "Some man tried to—" She buried her face against his shoulder.

Isaiah got a flash of dark brown luminous eyes, then her long black hair fell over her soft cheeks and hid part of her face. Her beauty startled him. He didn't realize that he was staring at her until Noam explained, "She's a member of our tribe. We told her to wait for us on that hill over there, away from the crowd."

Eliakim brought him back to reality. "Isaiah, your father is waiting."

"Yes, I stayed long at the Temple. I stopped to pray for the success of our mission." He drew Eliakim closer to him. "Listen, you may not believe this but," Isaiah lowered his voice, "I saw the cherubim spread their wings and fly towards me. Once before I thought I had seen them move but today I was sure."

"Oh, come on now," Eliakim laughed. "You got too much smoke in your eyes from the incense altar." He pulled at Isaiah's hand. "You better do some flying before your father comes hunting for you."

As Isaiah started off, the girl called out, "Beware, Tiglath-Pileser is a tiger and Judah is but a lamb at his feet."

Isaiah was again captivated by the delicacy of her face. It wasn't until he had mounted his horse that her remark struck him as odd.

As the caravan started off, led by Chephren, an Egyptian who was noted for his trade and travel experience, Isaiah caught sight of Shebna watching them from the top of a high boulder. Isaiah frowned. That was the direction from which the girl had fled. But certainly Shebna wouldn't be so foolish as to molest the girl. The image of her striking face returned to him once more. Such beauty could be tempting. But Isaiah thrust the ugly thought from him. Yet why hadn't Shebna come down to bid them farewell properly? There was bad feeling between them, but Shebna had been brought up to be polite, with manners befitting a nobleman. Shebna and he had been taught by the same scribe. Isaiah had seen through Shebna's false outer mask on many occasions, but the fact that Shebna had not said good-by troubled him.

As his horse trod along, Isaiah was occupied in keeping up with the caravan. Part of the way was rough, and sudden ravines seemed to open below their feet. The countryside was desolate and the earth so dry that it cracked as the horses' hoofs passed over. How much remained yet to be done in Judah! What had the girl said? "Judah is but a lamb at the feet of Tiglath-Pileser." She was right, but someday Judah would be a tiger.

Isaiah's father drew alongside him. "Not much to see yet but we will be stopping as often as we can at some of the towns and villages along the way."

After an hour more of traveling, a thick haze settled around them. Isaiah saw Eben, his father and Chephren hold a quick consultation. Chephren put his fingers to his lips and blew a shrill whistle. The animals were slowly gathered into a circle. "We must find shelter immediately," Chephren warned. "A storm is coming."

Isaiah pointed to the black mountains. "We could find safety up there."

Chephren shook his head. "Safety from the storm perhaps, but not safety from the hill tribes who prey on unwary travelers."

Isaiah looked up. The sun was a hot red ball in the sky

behind the veil of haze. A storm seemed unlikely and yet
Chephren was wise in the ways of the desert and mountains.
He had made the trip to Damascus, and Babylon and even
farther, many times.

As Isaiah was wondering if there would really be a storm,
it broke upon them with savage fury. They huddled close
against the wall of the mountain while the rain slashed down
in violent gusts. The breeze felt good and the rain was re-
freshing. Isaiah went out into the buffeting storm until he
was drenched to the skin.

Then as suddenly as it had come, it stopped. The sun
blazed forth again, hotter and redder than before. The
camels unstretched their long awkward legs; Chephren
clicked his teeth and the procession of camels and donkeys
started off. Within a few hours, everything that had gotten
wet was leather-dry.

The next day they were warmly welcomed at a village and
invited to stay for several days, but Amoz thanked the vil-
lagers and they went on.

The scorching heat began to weaken them. It was decided
to travel during dawn and evening, and rest during mid-
afternoon until they reached a cooler part of the country.

On the fourth day, the caravan traveled until exhausted,
hoping to reach an oasis. Finally, Amoz insisted they call a
halt. They made camp for the night in the desert.

After the evening meal, the men stretched out on their
straw mats. The camel drivers lay down on the ground,
using their cloaks as a covering. Isaiah unrolled a rug for his
father and himself. Feeling restless, Isaiah went for a walk
among the sand dunes. There was so much to see, so much
to remember, about this country he loved. When Isaiah
returned, the ashes of their fire, on which they had roasted

a lamb, were dying. All looked peaceful. Afraid of disturbing his sleeping father, Isaiah took his bed mat to the far
side, near the animals. Their regular heavy breathing rose
in the still, hushed air. As Isaiah stretched out, a sense of
brooding fell on him and sleep would not come. Finally, he
dozed off and it surprised him that the last thing he thought
of was the young Rechabite girl.

Fitfully, Isaiah rolled over. For a sudden, startled moment, he thought he had cried out in his sleep. Then he
realized groggily that it was only one of the donkeys bray-
ing. He rubbed his eyes, still fogged with sleep. Something
seemed to be moving behind the donkey. A shadow, a figure.

Isaiah leaped up. The flames of the fire were nearly out.
The guards seemed to be dozing. Their heads bobbed and
nodded on their chests.

Isaiah ran behind the donkey. A leather pouch lay on the
ground, where it had been dropped in haste. A few yards
away, Isaiah saw a slight figure disappear behind a sandy
hillock. Isaiah saw two other figures up ahead, waiting for
the running man. Could he chance it? If there were three
men, he could make it, but were there more? Recklessly, he
plunged after the man. There was a cry of warning from
one of the lookouts as Isaiah pounced on the short figure
before him. The man's face and head were tightly wrapped
up in a cotton cloth. Only the man's eyes gleamed through.
Isaiah tore away at the cloth. It was not the kind that was
woven locally but in Egypt or some foreign country. Isaiah
was puzzled. If this were a bandit, he would not own such
fine cloth. And why would someone go to such great lengths
to cover his face? What was he hiding?

The lithe figure under Isaiah threw him back. Isaiah

stumbled. The man's fist crashed into his face and Isaiah fell backward, his ankle twisting under him.

Isaiah lunged for the man, and then they were both rolling in the dirt.

Where is everybody? Isaiah wondered. Why don't the guards hear? It was then that a sweet, sickening smell came over him. The man or boy—he was so supple and small that it was hard to judge—had a wet cloth in his hand and was pushing it into Isaiah's face. It made Isaiah feel dizzy. Some drug obviously, Isaiah thought, pulling back. As he did so, his foot snapped under him and he couldn't help crying out with the intense pain.

Summoning all his power, Isaiah staggered up and clutched at that cloth covering. The figure somehow felt familiar. Those strong arms reminded him—but he must know for sure. He must be able to identify more than those glittering eyes. But as he grappled, his hand kept slipping from the cloth. The cloying smell numbed his senses. His hand felt heavy. It dropped from the cloth and fell for a moment on the man's neck. Isaiah felt something and his fingers tightened, tightened. Tugging with all his ebbing strength, he fell back in a faint, a lapis lazuli amulet of Pazuzu clutched in his hand.

It wasn't until many hours later that Isaiah was found. The guards had been drugged and when they came to, they raised the alarm. Isaiah dragged himself into a sitting position as his father and Eben approached, but when he tried to stand, his foot buckled under him.

Eben looked at the swollen ankle and shook his head. "It looks bad," he said. "It may be broken. But then you know more about medicine than I do, Amoz."

"I have picked up some bits of information here and

there. I'll see what I can do," Amoz said. "We must put on cold compresses at once, then I'll make a splint."

"I'm all right," Isaiah insisted. "What happened?"

"I thought *you* could tell us," his father said.

"I'm not sure," Isaiah wiped his damp brow. He realized from the heavy perspiration that he was feverish. "I heard someone at the donkeys. I awoke—" He gasped as he recalled the struggle with the man. "What did he take?"

His father hesitated. "Nothing much, really. That's the strange thing. If they were robbers, they would have taken the gold and silver plates. They touched nothing but the pouch with the royal seal on it. That's of value to no one but me."

Isaiah pulled himself up with a great effort. The mounting fever glazed his eyes. "What if someone were to use those papers to gain an audience with Tiglath-Pileser? What if someone were to tell the King lies? Try to stir up trouble."

"That's a lot of nonsense. Your fever is giving you delusions."

"But what if the papers fell into the wrong hands?" Isaiah persisted, thinking of the amulet.

Amoz shrugged. "They couldn't do much. At best, if by chance, they should reach Nineveh before us, we would prove them imposters when we arrived, and then where would they be? No," Amoz applied a cold cloth to Isaiah's foot, "it's too farfetched. I'm not interested in fancies so much as facts. I want those culprits apprehended. We're going to make camp here for a few days. It will give you a chance to rest your foot. In the meantime, we'll make inquiries in the villages nearby to see what information we can gain."

"Then you are concerned about the missing papers?" Isaiah guessed shrewdly.

"Yes, papers with the royal seal of Judah on them should not be on the loose in some market place," Amoz said. "It may make our entrance into Tiglath-Pileser's court more difficult. But we are carrying costly gifts, fit only for a king, so there should be no trouble."

"There are many rich enemies of Judah who could try to bribe Tiglath-Pileser with gifts of gold and silver," Isaiah pointed out. "Why should he trust us?"

Amoz stood up before his son, his blue eyes bright and hard. "Because I'm a man of honor and trust."

Days passed but the men whom Amoz sent out returned with no news of the stolen papers. At last, the caravan had to move on.

"We'll have to change our route," Chephren suggested. "We'll avoid the well-traveled paths and take a longer, more circuitous way."

Reluctantly, Amoz agreed. "We should return to Jerusalem," Eben said cautiously. "I don't like going into a foreign country without the protection of papers from our King."

"We have already lost much time," Amoz said. "The sooner we get to Nineveh, the better."

As the days lengthened into weeks and the weeks into months, Isaiah thought they would never reach the city on the Tigris. As much as his father tended his foot, Isaiah could not bear to stand on it. The pain was excruciating and slowly a black circle had spread around his ankle. Isaiah knew his father was greatly worried that poison had set in.

At last, they reached the royal city of Assyria. Although he was weary, and his foot throbbed painfully, Isaiah thrilled at the splendor of this great city. Lush farms and gardens spread out on each side of the Tigris. Magnificent statues of Babylonian gods seemed to be everywhere. Huge temples with richly decorated walls blazed in startling shades of blue and red. Straggly-bearded sorcerers wandered the streets, mumbling incantations.

As their caravan passed through the arched portals of one of the entrance gates, they were stopped. A crowd gathered in minutes. Before they had been in Nineveh an hour, the news of their arrival had spread through the market place and penetrated even the walls of the royal palace.

"Could you please tell me where I can find a good physician at once?" Amoz asked a curious bystander.

A man stepped out of the crowd. He looked at Isaiah's foot. "There's only one man who can help you. We are noted for our medicine. But one of the Court physicians is from Samaria."

"A Samaritan?" Amoz asked surprised.

"Yes," the man nodded. "Obed was brought here as a slave. But he learned much about medicine from his father. Now he's one of the Court physicians most favored by Tiglath-Pileser." He beckoned. "I'll show you the way."

"Go ahead," Eben said. "Yuval and I will take care of making provisions for the animals. Where will we meet?"

"At the royal palace," Amoz said. "I would like to arrange for an audience with Tiglath-Pileser as soon as possible."

"Good," Eben agreed. "I have not felt easy since the loss of the royal papers. We must explain and settle this matter at once."

"First I will take care of Isaiah, then I will meet you," Amoz said.

"You will have to make an appointment with the Sukkallu, the King's chamberlain," the man, standing at their side, said.

"Yes, thank you," Amoz said. "I know that to reach your king is not easy."

"My king," the man spat. "My dog!"

Amoz stared at him in astonishment.

"Forgive me," the man added quickly, glancing around anxiously. "I'm a poor peasant from the hills."

"You do not speak like a peasant, and you know the ways of the Court," Amoz pointed out.

The man lowered his voice. "My name is Samsi-Hadad. It may be meaningless to you. But I am related to the former Babylonian king, Nabonassar. Once I was a courtier but I dared to speak out against the Assyrian assassin and—" He stopped. "No matter, let me help your boy. I can see that his foot needs immediate attention." He waved them on. "Obed has only a small apartment in the back of the palace courtyard. But his fame is great."

He led the way through the palace courtyard and around to the back of the palace grounds.

Amoz took Isaiah's hand. "Do not be ashamed to lean on me," he said.

A bushy, gray-haired, blue-eyed man appeared at the sound of voices outside his door. "A patient for you," Samsi-Hadad said with a smile, "from Judah."

"From Judah?" Obed gasped.

"Yes," Amoz said. "I have come from the court of King Jotham to bring welcome to King Tiglath-Pileser. My son had an accident on the way. I doctored his foot as best I could but my knowledge of medicine is limited."

"From Judah," Obed said under his breath, as if it were a benediction. He touched Amoz's shoulder. "A Hebrew.

Come, come in. I would like to talk to you. I would like to know what is new in Israel. I have heard much that is disturbing but at this distance one never knows what is true and what is false."

"It's not distance that makes the difference," Amoz said. "Sometimes one can't tell what is true and what is false, even with neighbors."

"Yes," Obed nodded. "Where's the rest of your party?"

"The men are making arrangements for the animals. I want to go to the Court at once. Perhaps the Sukkallu can tell us where to get lodging."

Obed hesitated. "Who is the One God?" he asked suddenly.

Amoz stared at him in astonishment. "There is but one God, the Lord of Hosts, the Holy One of Israel," Isaiah interrupted heatedly.

"What kind of nonsense is this?" Amoz demanded.

Obed sighed. "There's no point in my trying to test you. My heart tells me you are flesh of my flesh, and blood of my blood. I must warn you therefore."

"About what?" Amoz asked.

"First let me make your son comfortable."

"You don't need to hide anything from Isaiah," Amoz said.

"I must warn you that a man claiming to be an ambassador from the Court of Judah came here only two days ago, bearing documents and presents from King Jotham. When he was presented, he rushed forth and attempted to stab Tiglath-Pileser."

"But that's impossible," Amoz said, "and disastrous. I must see Tiglath-Pileser at once to set things straight. Such an incident can lead to war."

"No, wait a while," the doctor advised. "You'll be safe in my apartment. Don't see the King until his temper cools."

"No, no," Amoz insisted. "I must tell the others. I'll go to see the King myself. I will warn Eben and Yuval so they can take over in case of—in case of any trouble."

"I will take care of your son's foot at once. I will keep him here with me. If you need help, you can depend on me."

After Amoz had left, Obed motioned to Isaiah. "Come into my inner chamber," Obed spread out his hands. "This is my world."

Isaiah hobbled after the doctor. He saw long strings of herbs and vegetables drying from a rack on the wall. There were rows after rows of varicolored substances in glass jars and bottles of all sizes. His eye fell on a scalpel that was lying on a small marble table. Isaiah couldn't help shuddering.

"The probe is good for puncturing abscesses," the doctor explained, watching Isaiah. He propped Isaiah's foot up on a pillow. He unwound the bandage that Amoz had improvised. "Your father did a good job," Obed said. Isaiah twinged as the bandage caught. "Ah, yes, tender, wait a moment. I'll get some olive oil. That will help to soak off the dressing."

"My mother," Isaiah said, "used to give me olive oil as a gargle whenever I had a sore throat."

"I myself recommend plain goat's milk for bad coughs but olive oil is good for many things. Oil or wine can clean out many infections."

"Do you think it's dangerous for my father to see King Tiglath-Pileser now? What harm do you think could come to him?"

The physician pointedly ignored his query. "Perhaps if you're here long enough, I can show you some of the many herbs I have, and I've gotten excellent extracts from animals, and—"

"What do you think he would do?" Isaiah persisted. "My father is a trusting man. No matter how many times his trust has been violated, he is still as innocent as if he had never been duped or taken advantage of."

"Don't worry. Everything will work out well. If you like, as soon as I finish putting a poultice on your ankle, I will go to the Court chamber myself. I don't have much influence. When young I was brought here as a captive slave. But I have risen in the King's Court because of my knowledge of medicine." He sighed. "I'm lucky. As long as the King stays well and I keep him well, everything is fine. Should he fall ill and I'm not able to cure him, I could lose my life."

"A friend of mine, Shebna," Isaiah said, "whose father was a Babylonian, told me that once the King had a doctor's arm cut off because he did not help some noble get well."

"Yes," the doctor said, handing Isaiah a mixture in a glass. "They have a strict code of laws here."

Isaiah smelled the liquid and shook the glass so that the mixture rose and fell in small waves. "What is this?"

"Do you distrust me?" Obed smiled.

"No, I'm curious."

"It's mostly barley water with a touch of licorice and," the doctor's blue eyes gleamed, "some secret ingredients I cannot divulge."

Isaiah took a test swallow. "It's not bad," he said. "What will it do for me?"

"It'll make you feel better," Obed said. "Now let's get

that leg in shape so you can walk on it without being too uncomfortable."

There was a sudden hubbub outside and Eben came rushing into the room. "They've imprisoned Amoz," he gasped. "Yuval fled when he heard the news. I don't know where." He paused for breath. "I was told that you were keeping Isaiah safe here. We must hide him."

"No, no," Obed said. "Sit down a moment. I'll bring you a glass of wine. We must be calm."

"Can you do anything?"

"Perhaps. I don't know." He hesitated. "Yes, I do know. Of course, I'll help. I'll see the King myself."

"I don't want to endanger your life, but if only he can be convinced that we are genuine representatives from the Court of King Jotham—"

Obed's eye lighted on Isaiah. "Come, you will help me. You will go to the King with me. Certainly he will understand that no father puts his only son in a dangerous situation like this. Are you willing?"

"Of course," Isaiah said eagerly.

"First we must try to get into the dungeons to see your father. They are below the palace kitchens."

"I have 400 shekels of silver with me, if it will help," Eben said.

"Money always helps, unfortunately," Obed sighed. "You wait here for us, or if you like I will send my young assistant out with you and you can look for your friend."

"I think I would rather wait," Eben said. "I'm too worried to think straight now."

The 400 shekels of silver paved the way for Obed and Isaiah to reach the dungeon where Amoz had been imprisoned. "Just a few moments," the guard warned.

"I don't understand," Amoz said, bewildered, after he had thanked Obed for coming to his rescue. "King Tiglath-Pileser welcomed me warmly at first. I told him that Judah would not engage in any alliances with other nations against him. I explained how we were anxious to live in peace. And he led me on fawningly. When I had explained my mission carefully and as best I could, he pounced on me, storming, 'You speak like a man who can be trusted, yet I trusted the other Judean who came.'"

"I don't think he was a Judean," Obed said. "After they threw him to the wild dogs, his remains were turned over to me. I found a lapis lazuli amulet on him of one of the Babylonian gods."

The guard came racing down the dark, narrow passageway. "Quick, flee!" he shouted. "The King himself is coming. Someone must have been spying on us."

But even as Obed and Isaiah turned, their passage was blocked by the King and the royal guards. "What are you doing here?" Tiglath-Pileser demanded.

"I thought I might help this man," Obed said. "He brought his son to me. His ankle was badly infected. The boy's father told me he was from the Court of Judah and that he wanted an audience with you." Obed hesitated for a moment, then added, "I told him about the false emissary who had been here before him and in spite of this, he went to you."

"I see." Tiglath-Pileser pointed to Isaiah, "And this is his son?"

"Yes, and as a father, you know well that no man would travel so many miles with his own son and put him in danger," Obed said boldly.

Tiglath-Pileser looked at him craftily. "How do I know this is his son? Perhaps it is only a slave."

"I will do anything to prove that I am Isaiah, son of Amoz," Isaiah said.

Tiglath-Pileser stared at the tall, strong boy before him. "Are you willing to prove your father's innocence by submitting to the water test?"

"Yes, anything," Isaiah said quickly. "My father came here on a mission of peace. I shall prove the truth of what my father has said."

"Your Majesty, I beg your humble pardon," Obed put in. "But I do not think Isaiah knows what the water test is."

"He'll have a chance to find out tomorrow morning. He'll be thrown into the Tigris three times. If he floats, then the father is innocent. If he sinks, the father will die along with the boy."

"Subject *me* to some kind of test, but not my son," Amoz protested. "We don't have the sea near us, as you do. We have no mighty rivers. Many of our river beds are dry most of the year. My son does not know how to swim."

Tiglath-Pileser laughed. "Then pray to your God to teach him how overnight."

When they returned to the doctor's room, they found Eben in a daze. "How can he treat emissaries like this?" he said, when he heard the news.

"We are only a speck of a country," Isaiah said. "That's why he feels he can step on us; and yet our smallness will make us great."

"What can we do?" Eben turned to the doctor. "Is there no way to smuggle Isaiah into the hills somehow?"

"No," Isaiah protested. "The minute I am found missing, my father will die. There is a way. If you have faith, if you believe in the One God, He will open the way for you."

Isaiah bowed his head. "I know this for my father has taught it to me. Things shall go well for the righteous. *For they shall eat the fruit of their doings.*" When Isaiah raised his head, his eyes were glowing with bright determination. "I know this, too. *God is my salvation. I will not be afraid. The Lord is my strength.* I'm going to learn how to swim to-night."

"But how?" Eben asked.

"What's the most important thing to know about swimming?" Isaiah asked the doctor.

"How to breathe properly. If you could hold your breath under water long enough—" The doctor's hands trembled. "There is a way." He reached for a deep, round silver bowl. "As soon as I fill this with water, it will be your river. I will show you how to breathe out and breathe in. By morning you will be able to swim with the fish in the sea."

At dawn, a royal guard called for Isaiah. His father was already standing on the banks of the river. Tiglath-Pileser was seated at his side. A large skin boat was waiting. At a signal, Isaiah was put in the boat and rowed out, until Tiglath-Pileser raised his right hand and the men stopped.

One of the men in the boat grabbed Isaiah by the waist. "Spare him," Amoz cried out in agony, his voice carrying across the still water. "I have lived out my life. I'm willing to die for my country. Let my boy live."

Tiglath-Pileser raised his left hand and the man released Isaiah and the boat started back to shore.

"A young man who is willing to die for his father and an old man who is willing to die for his country are worth sparing," Tiglath-Pileser said. "We may need Judah's help at some time. We will count on you. Now come to my Court and Tiglath-Pileser will show you how a king entertains ambassadors from beyond our shores."

She sat before the tent door, weaving narrow
strips of new tent cloth.

Chapter 3

The warm way in which the King of Assyria made all of his palace open to Amoz was like the sun coming out after a storm. Amoz and Isaiah, along with the others in their caravan, were allowed to roam freely about the city and into the outskirts, and much of what he saw troubled Amoz.

The Turtan, commander of the Assyrian army, proudly showed Amoz and Isaiah their military storehouses.

As they passed aisle after aisle of chariots, the Turtan turned to Isaiah. "This is enough to make a young man's blood boil, isn't it?" He stopped before a chariot overlaid with gold. "Are beauties like this known in your country?"

Isaiah hesitated. He had to be careful how he answered. Perhaps the Turtan was indirectly seeking military information about Judah. "We don't have many chariots," he answered truthfully. "They are best for battle in flat country." Isaiah glanced at the rows of chariots spread out before him. In his mind's eye, he could see them filled with the drivers and the bowmen and the shield-bearers, sweeping down closer, ever closer, to destroy whatever country they wished. He turned to the Turtan. "We are a mountainous country," he said smoothly. "These chariots would not be of much use against Jerusalem."

The Turtan nodded and went on into another storeroom. "But these," he said, pointing to the swords, spears and lances, hanging on the walls, "these would be good against any country." He strode forward and plucked at the strings of a bow. "These bows are made of the finest woods. You used the cedars of Lebanon to make your Temple." His eyes narrowed. "We use the finest woods to make our bows."

Isaiah stepped forward to look more closely at an ornately designed sword. "So," the Turtan laughed, "I knew it. You are interested in military weapons."

Isaiah's voice was soft. "I'm more interested in how we can beat these swords into plowshares." He whirled around and picked up a spear with a bronze head. He held it lightly as if he were about to fling it at the Turtan. For a moment, the commander was thrown off his guard and he drew back. "I'm interested in how this spear can be turned into a pruning fork." Isaiah dropped it and the ringing sound echoed on the stone floor. Isaiah's father looked at him astounded. His heart swelled with pride. No matter what happened to him now—no matter how many short or long years remained to him—he knew that Judah would be in safe hands.

"Show me your granaries," Isaiah said. "I'm a farmer at heart. I like to see wheat growing in the fields instead of the harsh glitter of bronze helmets."

"You surprise me," the Turtan said. "You talk like a peasant—yet you are the son of a nobleman."

"There's nothing nobler in the world," Amoz said, "than seeking peace. If you don't mind, we'll go back to the palace to rest."

But in the rooms of the palace that had been set aside for them, Isaiah and his father found no rest. "Those spears and chariots are not going to stand there," Isaiah said. "Tiglath-Pileser will use them."

"But not against us," Amoz said. "He has given me his solemn word. I have a letter of friendship from him to King Jotham, promising that he will not war against Judah, and guaranteeing to protect us from any others who might strike against us."

"How much tribute does he expect for this letter of friendship?" Isaiah stormed.

"Much, much," Amoz shrugged his shoulders. "But it's the only way. It's cheaper to buy peace with silver than with our country's blood."

"When will we learn not to make war any more?" Isaiah cried out.

Amoz looked at him strangely. "It will never come to pass."

"Perhaps *it shall come to pass in the end of days,*

That the mountain of the Lord's house shall be established as the top of the mountains,

And shall be exalted above the hills;

And all nations shall flow unto it."

"These are wondrous things you say," his father said. "Where did these ideas come to you?"

"I don't know. The words have been whirling around in my brain. The more I have seen of the glories of Assyria, the more tortured I have felt. How can we live side by side with them in this world?"

His father sat down on a low stool. "I would like to take

your words down and preserve them, Isaiah," he said. "They are too precious to lose."

"They are burned across my mind," Isaiah said. "Now that I have seen Assyria's might, I know there is only one way. *Many peoples shall go and say:*

'Come ye, and let us go up to the mountain of the Lord,
To the house of the God of Jacob;
And He will teach us of His ways,
And we will walk in His paths.'
For out of Zion shall go forth the law,
And the word of the Lord from Jerusalem."

Isaiah's voice rang out clear and true, like the sound of the trumpet signaling the start of a religious festival.

"And he shall judge between the nations,
And shall decide for many peoples;
And they shall beat their swords into plowshares,
And their spears into pruning hooks;
Nation shall not lift up sword against nation,
Neither shall they learn war any more."

Amoz rocked back and forth on the stool. "You make me long for my home. The green lushness of these fields is no longer a delight to my eyes. I want to feel the hard, dry soil of Judah under my feet and to crush the brown earth in my hands. I will tell Eben and Yuval to make immediate arrangements for our departure."

"I would like to say good-by to Obed," Isaiah said.

"Obed," Amoz plucked at his beard thoughtfully. "He, too, longs for his home," he said. "If only there were some way that we could help him. Let's go together and see what service we may be able to give him in return for his courtesies to us."

Obed guessed the reason for their call as soon as Amoz

and Isaiah came into his room. "You are planning to leave," he said flatly.

"Yes," Amoz nodded. "I want to know if there is something that we can do for you before we leave."

Obed smiled wryly. "Could you take me on wings and drop me in Israel?" He shrugged. "I'm a fool to think of this. Even if it could be, I know that my country is greatly changed. It holds too many sad memories for me. I was only a boy when I was taken captive. I wouldn't remember much. It would be stranger for me there than here and yet—" He turned away, his voice dry and choking. "It is the home of my birth and as foolish as it is, I would like to see it before the end of my days. But don't let me mar our good-bys with this sadness." He went into the inner chamber where he kept his medicines. "Excuse me for a moment. I have something for you," he called over his shoulder. He brought out several jars and bottles. "These should come in handy on your travels back. Your food may not be of the best and it might be wise to take a purgative at least once or twice a month."

"I have heard of the Egyptians doing this," Amoz said. "I'm surprised that you—"

"I don't scorn *any* knowledge," Obed replied. "And you're right about the Egyptians. Many of them take salts of antimony or calomel three times a month. They believe that by purging their bodies, they will rid themselves of any diseases that may come from the food they eat. I don't think they're completely right, neither do I think they're completely wrong. It won't hurt for you to have some of my special quinine, cloves and cardamom seed on hand for emergency use."

"I wish there were some way for you to come along with

us," Amoz sighed. "For selfish reasons. I know there's nothing that you can do for Uzziah, but King Jotham is not in the best of health and another doctor's opinion—"

"And Uriah, the Temple priest, would like to have some doctor tell him what he can do about the pains in his feet and hands," Isaiah said.

"Uriah can do nothing but suffer unless he wishes to leave the priesthood," Obed said. "The priests wash their hands and feet dozens of times a day before they enter the sanctuary, and then they walk barefoot on the cold stones. Year after year, the cold penetrates and their bones become stiff and rheumatic."

"Rheumatic?" Amoz repeated.

"Yes, we call it arthritis. Nothing can be done for it. One just has to endure it, as I endure my life here."

As they took their leave of Obed laden down with many packets and bottles and advice, Amoz, followed by Isaiah, walked along aimlessly. Isaiah noticed that they were in the royal gardens and not headed for their rooms, but he made no comment. Seeing that his father was deep in thought, Isaiah took the medicines and sat down on a limestone bench. Amoz wandered down a tree-shaded passage, his head bent. Suddenly, he heard his name called. Amoz turned startled and Isaiah hurried to his side. Tiglath-Pileser strolled up to them slowly. "I see that you are taking advantage of our gardens before you leave. Do you know that we have trees and plants here from many different parts of the world?" He gazed at Amoz meaningfully. "In time, every tree and flower from all over the world will be planted here. But," he put out his hand, "Judah need have no fear of me or of any of her enemies. If a country raises such men as your son and you, she deserves to remain unmolested."

"Your words will please King Jotham," Amoz said.

"Is there anything that I can do to please you before your departure?" Tiglath-Pileser asked. "You may have any gift in my kingdom that you wish."

Amoz looked directly at Tiglath-Pileser. "If I asked for a gift greater than gold and silver and worth more than all your kingdom, would you still give it to me?"

"Riddle me no riddles," Tiglath-Pileser snapped. "I promised you anything in my kingdom."

"I ask for the freedom of the slave Obed."

Tiglath-Pileser smiled. "I will tell you something—that man has always been free." He raised his right hand. "Obed is free." He turned to the royal scribe, who was at his side. "See that this order is carried out immediately."

That night, there was much rejoicing. Amoz, Obed, Eben and Yuval sat around deep into the night, talking, talking, talking. Obed's voice sounded fresh and young, as if he had been reborn. Isaiah had sat himself in a corner, eager to listen to the exchange of ideas that flowed back and forth as the wine poured back and forth, but soon he found his head nodding and only fragments of their conversation reached his ears.

Amoz expressed his satisfaction with their mission but Yuval sounded moody and skeptical. "I don't trust him. I can't forget the way we were received at first. Judah is like a thorn in the lion's paw. He will have to pluck it out."

Isaiah lifted his head. Somewhere before he had heard something like that. Yes, the Rechabite girl, the one with the shining brown eyes. She had said that Judah is but a lamb. Isaiah's eyes grew heavy again and he decided to go to bed. As he started forward on heavy feet, he heard his father say, "Judah is small. That is our strength. If we stand alone, we are not worth troubling. If we join with others and make a big noise, then we will be lost."

"That's exactly what Tiglath-Pileser wants," Eben said. "He wants us to be alone and defenseless so that he can attack us when he wishes."

Amoz turned to Obed. "You know Tiglath-Pileser better than all of us. What do you think?"

"I think that he wants to swallow the world. I have heard rumors that he has designs on Egypt—"

"See," Eben said, "if that should be so, Judah will be in his way."

Isaiah stood still. "Oh, when shall nation *not lift up sword against nation?*"

"What did you say?" Eben asked, glancing up.

"Good night," Isaiah mumbled as he left the room.

But if Isaiah felt he had missed anything that night, he more than made it up on their way back to Jerusalem. Night after night, the men would gather around the fire and Obed would ceaselessly ask about food and fashions, holidays and health, world politics and water pollution. Even Isaiah sometimes had to laugh at Obed's enthusiasm.

"I can't wait to taste bread, the way it is baked by the Hebrew women, and wafers with honey—now that's a treat."

"Flour is flour," Eben laughed, poking Obed in his paunch. "You don't look starved."

"No, I was treated well once they knew of my medical skill, but only the Hebrew women know how to make the best cheese from goat's milk and—"

"It won't be long now," Amoz said. "Things have gone well for us. Chephren says that with good luck we may reach Jerusalem in three or four more days."

Now that home was so close, the men traveled longer hours willingly. Early one afternoon, Chephren suggested that they detour from the caravan route and seek out a well that lay off the beaten path. "We've been driving the animals too hard," he said. "Let's take a brief rest."

Amoz agreed and so they headed for the oasis. As they approached, a half-circle of oak trees which was planted around the well site cast a leafy welcome.

"This looks like one of the areas built up by King Uzziah," Amoz said. "There's so much I'll have to tell him."

"I know you want to push on," Eben said. "But I'm glad we're stopping. It'll do us good. We won't come into Jerusalem exhausted."

As they came closer, they saw a settlement of tents grouped near the well. "Perhaps we can get some advance news of home," Amoz said eagerly, as an old man walked up to greet them.

"Why, that's Yael, Noam's father," Isaiah shouted, jumping off his horse.

"Peace be with you," Yael said. "It's good to see your faces again. All Jerusalem is waiting for news of your journey."

Amoz put out his hand in warm welcome. "All has gone well. I would like to hear news, if you have any for us, of home."

"We have been here for many weeks," Yael said, "but merchants traveling back and forth bring us news, even though it may be a little out of date. Ahaz, Jotham's son, has gotten himself into some difficulties lately. It seems that he's become friendly with Shebna and—"

"Shebna!" Isaiah burst out. "Nothing could be worse. Ahaz is foolish but harmless. Shebna, on the other hand, is clever. If Ahaz should become King—"

Yael embraced him. "Don't worry yourself about these things now. It may only be talk—and enough of talk for now. Come, we'll take care of your horses. The women will bring out fresh meat and goat's cheese."

Obed laughed, "See, my wish is coming true already."

As the men went into Yael's tent, he turned to Isaiah. "Noam is with the sheep on the hills behind the tents. Go ahead and surprise him."

Briskly, Isaiah started off. As he passed the last tent, set off from the others, he saw the brown-eyed girl, who had lingered in his memory. She sat before the tent door, weaving narrow strips of new tent cloth.

He hesitated. "Good day," he said.

She nodded, not taking her eyes from the loom. "Is it good for the Holy One of Israel?"

Isaiah was startled by her reply. The sun glinted on her long, black hair. Isaiah stepped closer. "I would like to talk with you," he began.

Just then there was a wild shout from the hills and Isaiah knew that Noam must have spotted the caravan and was coming down to see for himself what was going on.

Reluctantly, Isaiah turned. When Noam, shading his eyes with his hands from the bright sun, recognized Isaiah, he rushed down the grassy slope and threw himself against Isaiah breathlessly. "How good it is to see you," he panted. "Like manna from heaven. It's been so lonely up in the hills the last few days." He laughed. "I've begun to talk to myself." He put his arm around Isaiah. "Come to our tent. My mother will be happy to see you."

"My father and the others are there," Isaiah said. "Perhaps we could just sit here." He pointed to a smooth grassy spot that faced the girl's tent.

Noam's eyes wandered to where the girl sat, busily weaving, seemingly unaware that they were nearby.

"The Nameless One has spoken of you much," Noam said, as they sat down, crisscrossing their legs.

"The Nameless One?" Isaiah frowned. "What do you mean?"

"It's a strange story," Noam said, keeping his voice down. "We found her and her mother starving in the desert. She was perhaps eight years old or more. At first, we thought they were poor travelers, and some even said they were a family of criminals or worse, but the girl knew how to read and write Hebrew, young as she was."

"You mean, she knows how to read and write Hebrew?" Isaiah asked, astonished.

"Yes, and that means some scribe must have taught her. Perhaps," Noam added significantly, "a royal scribe. Her mother's cloak was thin as a butterfly's wing, as if it had been woven by a highly skilled craftsman, and the colors in it glittered like the rainbow. It was the only legacy she left her daughter."

"Didn't the mother say anything about her daughter or herself?"

"No, she died just a few short months after they were found. She wouldn't say anything about where they had come from or what had happened to them. She wouldn't tell us her name or her daughter's name. She spoke rarely but well, as if she were highborn. My father made many inquiries after the mother's death, but who would want a young girl who was without family or name?—And so we call her the Nameless One."

Isaiah shook his head. "No, not nameless. She sounds like a prophetess to me. The few times that I have heard her speak, she has said strange things that disturb me. Perhaps God is using her to tell his thoughts to man."

"She knows much that does not come from learning," Noam said. "She can sense danger in the air. Many times she has protected us from attacks by wild animals, and human animals that rob other tribes."

Isaiah laughed. "You don't have to build her up for me. I'm already impressed. What you are talking about is only womanly intuition."

But Noam was very serious. "Wait, in time you will see what I mean." He stood up and his eyes lingered long on the girl. "She's very beautiful, isn't she?"

Something in the tone of his voice struck Isaiah. "Noam, are you in love with her?"

Noam nodded his head. "I'm afraid to say *yes* aloud but," he shrugged his shoulders, "she's not for me. I'm not worthy enough." He sighed. "Come along now. You've waited too long to taste some of my mother's cooking."

As they headed for Noam's tent, the girl stopped weaving and looked after them. "God be with you," she said, and then gazing at Isaiah's strong, broad back, she added softly, "God is with you."

"He's past awakening" Jacob said bitterly.

Chapter 4 /

Isaiah was not prepared for the lavish entertainment and riotous welcome that awaited them upon their return to Jerusalem. King Jotham gave a great feast in their honor, and day after day, his father was called by the Royal Council into conferences that lasted for hours and hours. Occasionally, his father invited Isaiah to come along and he listened patiently, and sometimes impatiently, to the seemingly endless discussions that circled around and around. The councilors were generally pleased with the results of Amoz's trip, although some of them felt, like Eben and Yuval, that Tiglath-Pileser could not be trusted.

Even Isaiah's Aunt Reba complained bitterly that she was not seeing enough of Amoz and that he would ruin his health going off to the palace and eating so much rich food.

"You want to do too much for us," Isaiah said to his aunt, after she had unburdened herself to Isaiah one afternoon.

"He's my only brother, how could I do too much for him or you?" his aunt said. "You have no idea how happy I was to come here and take care of you and your father after—" She paused. "It doesn't sound right saying it this way, but I know you understand. I loved your mother and grieved much for her, but for me it was a blessing being able to come here and look after this household. A widow is like a broken pot—useless, unwanted."

Isaiah patted her hand. "Anyway, you now have Obed to spoil."

"Yes," she said thoughtfully. "He's a fine man, but I wonder if he'll stay. He longs to return to Israel."

"If he goes, perhaps you'll go with him," Isaiah teased.

Isaiah was surprised to see his aunt blush. "Aunt Reba, how stupid of me," he said. "I would never have guessed—"

She fondly embraced him. "Now that you know my secret, I'll tell you one in return. Your father is planning a party in a fortnight to offer thanks for your safe return, and he has invited that lovely Rechabite family whom you met."

"I'm so weary of parties," Isaiah said. "All day long it goes on. I have begun to feel—
Woe unto them that rise up early in the morning,
That they may follow strong drink;
That tarry late into the night,
Till wine inflame them!"

"Your friends don't think this way," his aunt said. "Not even Eliakim. He enjoys a good time, as much as the others."

"Sure," Isaiah said, "*they regard not the work of the Lord,*
Neither have they considered the operation of His hands.
Therefore My people are gone into captivity,
For want of knowledge."

Reba shook her head. "I don't know whether you are blessed or cursed to have such thoughts. But I do know it won't make your life easier."

Isaiah laughed. "Would you like me to make your life easier? I know you will have a hundred things to think of with this party coming on. Would you like me to go see Jacob, the fruit vendor, and tell him to set aside his best grapes and melons and other fruits for the party?"

"You are a dear, but I can send my handmaiden to do that," Reba said.

"I would like an excuse to go out into the fields and orchards," Isaiah said, "so I'll take care of it." And off he went.

Isaiah walked with long strides. Soon he had left the narrow alleyways and the call of the market place behind. He waved to Daniel, a member of the royal council, whom he met in passing and whose perfumed beard and hair could not cover up the stench of too much wine. Isaiah thought of what he had just said to his aunt. But the day was too bright and the air was full of the promise of good things to come, so he hurried along. As he reached the fields outside the city, Isaiah stopped for a moment to breathe deeply and to feast on the green that slashed into the brown hillside.

As Isaiah cut through the fields, he saw Jacob in the distance and called to him. The man turned slowly. Isaiah saw that he was carrying a child in his arms.

Isaiah came forward quietly. "I hope I didn't awaken the child."

"He's past awakening," Jacob said bitterly. "He's dead."

"I'm sorry," Isaiah said. "Can I help you in any way?"

"Can you stop the princes from taking our land? Can you stop the judges from being bribed so that when we cry out for justice we are punished instead? You can sooner stop the sun from shining."

"What are these wild accusations?" Isaiah asked. "How can you speak this way?"

"Your voice is deeper and your body longer than when I last saw you, Isaiah. You have grown much—but have you grown in wisdom?"

"I'm willing to learn," Isaiah said, "from even a fruit vendor. When my mother was dying, my father came to you for pomegranates and figs to tempt her appetite. When I was born, it was fruits from your orchard that lay heaped on our table to refresh our guests."

Jacob shifted the burden in his arms. "This is Enos's son."

Isaiah turned in the direction of Enos's farm, shielding his eyes from the sun. "I see many workers in the fields. Surely things are well with him."

"The princes have taken over the fields on either side of me. Enos was driven out a few weeks ago with his family. His wife and two daughters went to live with relatives in Lachish. Enos stayed behind with his young son, who was too ill to travel. He begged the prince to allow him to stay in his home until his boy recovered, but the prince was in a hurry to tear down the old house and put up a new summer home and so Enos was thrown out."

"How is this possible?" Isaiah asked. "What happened then?"

"My wife took him in, but the boy was ill and we were afraid that my children would suffer, too. Finally, he had to leave. I don't know what happened after that. I heard only that Enos had stolen some wheat—wheat that he had grown with his own hands—from the prince's storehouse. He was caught. I have not seen him around since then, nor will I."

His face contorted. "He stole, if you can call it stealing, to keep his son from dying."

Isaiah opened his mouth but Jacob went on. "Don't tell me it's wrong. I know that it's wrong to steal a man's land from him."

Isaiah frowned. *"Woe unto them that join house to house,*
That lay field to field,
Till there be no room.
I'll talk to King Jotham about this as soon as I can."

"Don't stir up trouble for yourself," Jacob said. "These princes come with smiles on their faces and scraps of paper in their fists, and by sleight of hand the farms are swallowed up and made into fashionable estates." Jacob sighed. "I'll be next."

"I have heard some talk of this but I didn't believe it until now. I still don't believe this—in Jerusalem," Isaiah gasped.

Jacob thrust the boy's thin cold hand in Isaiah's. "Then believe this and remember it well. I found him in a corner of the market place, shriveled up like a dry prune. Even in death, there was no place for him."

Isaiah bowed his head. "I'll help you dig a grave, then I'll go to the Temple and ask Uriah to come and say a prayer."

"Don't pray for the boy," Jacob said. "It's too late. Pray for Jerusalem."

"You are right.
How is the faithful city
Become a harlot!
The ox knoweth his owner,
And the ass his master's crib;
But Israel doth not know."

As the day for the party approached, Isaiah felt even more depressed than before. He could not rid himself of the haunting image of the boy huddled in Jacob's arms. He would wake in the dead of night, a thin shadow from the saucer lamp on the table flickering in the room, and he would once again feel the cold hand of the child in his. Even the thought of seeing Noam and the girl again did not lessen his melancholy. The more he saw Reba and their cook preparing cakes for the feast, the more he lost his appetite. Even Amoz and Obed busied themselves with preparations for the party.

As occupied as he was, Amoz sensed that something was wrong with Isaiah, and the evening before the festivities, he took him aside. "You don't look well to me lately," Amoz said. "Your face is pale."

"It's Jerusalem that isn't well," Isaiah said.

"The whole head is sick,
And the whole heart faint,
From the sole of the foot even unto the head
There is no soundness in it."

"Save your poetry for the party," his father said. "Do you remember what you told me that day in Nineveh about nation not warring against nation? It would be well to repeat it at the party. There will be many close to the King at the party. They will forgive an old man for showing off his son." His father smiled. "Others will be there whom you would like to impress, too, I'm sure. There will be Dena, who can't take a step without her anklet bracelets calling attention to her shapely legs." He nudged Isaiah jokingly. "Don't tell me you haven't noticed her. Even Eliakim has stolen glances in her direction. And Adah, too—" His father smacked his lips. "Only the best."

The next night as Isaiah glanced about at those assembled at his father's table, at the women resplendent in their jewels, the men dressed in their finest linens of many hues,

he pondered, were these the best people in the land, as his
father had said? Was one of these men the one who had
taken away Enos's farm—and his son's life? He closed his
eyes for a moment, then woe to Jerusalem. Off in a corner
he saw Noam and Yael, and in the shadows, obscured almost
completely from his view, sat the Prophetess. What did they
think, he wondered?

All of a sudden, Isaiah felt his father tugging at his hand.
"Why so still? Our guests think it strange that you have
spoken barely two words the whole evening."

"What shall I tell them?" Isaiah asked, glancing around,
at the shining wine goblets, the silver bowls heaped with
fruit. "Shall I say

Your hands are full of blood.
Wash you, make you clean,
Put away the evil of your doings.
Cease to do evil;
Learn to do well;
Seek justice, relieve the oppressed,
Judge the fatherless, plead for the widow."

"At another time, your words would impress me," his
father said. "But you should think of more cheerful things
now. Look at the beauty before you." He nodded where
some of the women were sitting together. "Any one of those
women would make you a fine wife. Soon, Isaiah, it will be
time for you to think of marriage and you would do well to
consider any of the women who are under our roof tonight."

Isaiah's eyes wandered off to the shadowy corner where
the Nameless One sat. He sighed. "I'm sorry that I've dis-
appointed you. Is there anything I can do to make up for it?"

His father's face brightened. "Recite that poem about
turning swords into plowshares."

"This isn't the time or the place," Isaiah said.

"You don't need to feel modest," Amoz urged. "Our guests are your friends."

Before Isaiah could stop his father, he was tapping on a wine goblet and calling for silence. "We have heard Abner play his lyre tonight, and Jethro has entertained us with tales
There were encouraging shouts on all sides.
of King Solomon's day that were unknown even to me, and now I would like you to hear from my son."

"Isaiah has written a poem of sorts. I have shared my home with you, now let me share my heart."

Isaiah saw the glow in his father's eyes and knew that he had to meet the challenge in them—but what about the challenge from the Lord of Hosts?

Isaiah stood up, his strong body towering over the others. As he rose, a silence fell on the people. "Rather than tell you the poem my father mentioned, instead

Let me sing of my well-beloved."

"Good, that sounds good, go on," Daniel, one of the King's councilors, prodded.

"*My well-beloved had a vineyard
In a very fruitful hill.*"

Isaiah cleared his throat a bit self-consciously. Was he doing the right thing, he wondered? Was this the time to tell the princes of Jacob's suffering—of Jerusalem's agony?

He heard someone in the back of the room laugh. "Forgotten your lines already?"

Forgotten? Yes, righteousness and honesty were being forgotten and you didn't wait for a special time to remind people of it. You told them again and again whenever you could, wherever you could—even at a party in your father's house.

Isaiah's voice lifted high, as he repeated,

"My well-beloved had a vineyard
In a very fruitful hill;
And he digged it, and cleared it of stones,
And planted it with the choicest vine,
And built a tower in the midst of it,
And also hewed out a vat therein;
And he looked that it should bring forth grapes,
And it brought forth wild grapes."

"What do you mean wild grapes?" Daniel interrupted. "This sounded like a pleasant pastoral poem when you started but now—"

"Hush," a voice said in the back corner of the room and Isaiah was surprised to recognize it as the voice of the Nameless One.

"I'll be glad to explain in just a minute," Isaiah continued.
"O inhabitants of Jerusalem and men of Judah,
Judge, I pray you, betwixt me and my vineyard.
What could have been done more to my vineyard,
That I have not done in it?
Wherefore, when I looked that it should bring forth
*   grapes,*
Brought it forth wild grapes?"

Daniel laughed loudly. "You know, Isaiah, you're a clever one. That's the very question I asked you before. Now tell me what's the answer?"

Isaiah faced towards Daniel.
"I will tell you
What I will do to my vineyard:
I will take away the hedge thereof,
And it shall be eaten up;
I will break down the fence thereof,
And it shall be trodden down;

And I will lay it waste."

The silence in the room was like a living thing that could be touched and felt. Isaiah could hear the heavy breath of the men who had eaten too much and drunk too much wine.

"*It shall not be pruned nor hoed,*" Isaiah continued,
But there shall come up briers and thorns;
I will also command the clouds
That they shall rain no rain upon it."

Isaiah now turned away from Daniel and looking up and down the table, his black eyes fastened on each one in turn. "Need I tell you, Daniel, and honored guests that

The vineyard of the Lord of Hosts is the House of Israel,
And the men of Judah the plant of His delight;
And He looked for justice, but behold violence;
For righteousness, but behold a cry."

Isaiah bowed his head. He noticed that even his father seemed too stunned to say anything. What right did he have to spoil the party in this way? What right did he have to tell them that they had failed their God? He had already hurt his father enough and perhaps insulted their guests; if they realized what he meant, it applied to each of them. Nothing else he could do would be any worse and so he turned and walked up to the roof top. The night was black; the moon hidden behind a cloud, obscured as justice was now hidden in Jerusalem. Isaiah felt alone.

All at once, he felt rather than saw someone at his side. "The truth is not easy." He turned and saw the Nameless One.

"I'm sorry," he said.

"No," she shook her head. "Don't say that to me. I'm glad for what you said."

Isaiah looked at her and now the cloud had moved away from the moon and her face was illuminated as if by silver. "Didn't you understand that I said God would destroy the vineyard and that Judah was the vineyard?"

"Yes," she nodded, and her hair fell about her shoulders. "Shouldn't that be so? How can we seek justice from heaven, if we don't have it on earth?"

Isaiah's father joined them on the roof top. "Isaiah," he called, "our guests are leaving. I hope you will ask their forgiveness, for you have offended them."

"Have they asked God's forgiveness?" Isaiah asked.

The girl drew away silently. "Wait," Isaiah put out his hand. "I want to talk to you."

"There's no time," she said. "We're leaving at dawn."

She went back down the stairs before Isaiah could stop her.

"What has come over you?" his father asked sharply. "Has some maiden bewitched your thoughts so that they weave back and forth like wool on a loom?"

Isaiah laughed. "You mean that parade of beauties that you spread out before me like a feast? Father, did you really take a good look at them, strutting about with their

wanton eyes,
Walking and mincing as they go,
And making a tinkling with their feet."

"You haven't given them a chance," Amoz said. "All girls like to make up and look attractive."

"Do you call all those geegaws they wear—attractive? One of these days,

the Lord will take away the bravery of their anklets, and
the fillets, and the crescents, the pendants, and the bracelets,
and the veils, the headtires, and the armlets, and the sashes,

and the corselets, and the amulets; the rings, and the nose-
jewels; the aprons, and the mantelets, and the cloaks, and
the girdles; and the guaze robes, and the fine linen, and the
turbans, and the mantles."

"I agree with you that the trimmings are nothing but—"

"Do you also agree that

Instead of sweet spices there shall be rottenness;
And instead of a girdle rags;
And instead of curled hair baldness;
And instead of a stomacher a girding of sackcloth;
Branding instead of beauty?"

"You're making me lose my patience," his father said.
"I'm bewildered. Has someone also bewildered your sense?"

"Yes, maybe it's that," Isaiah said slowly. "Perhaps I
don't realize it myself."

"I thought so," his father said, his good humor returning.
"Tell me, who is it—Rachel with the fair skin, or Sapphira
with her tempting lips, who has gotten you so worked up
that you are gushing words like a fountain?"

"It's the Rechabite girl," Isaiah said.

His father was stunned. "You have your choice of the best
of the land, the noblest—"

"This is the best?" Isaiah shouted. "The best of what?"

"I will never ask for her hand in marriage for you," his
father said.

Isaiah could feel the muscles in his body tightening and
he felt as if he took one step, his bones would crack. "Then I
can't stay in this house any longer."

In the distance, a jackal howled and Isaiah shuddered.

"Isaiah," his father pleaded, "don't let a maiden come between us. Don't leave me because you love this girl."

"I'm leaving because I love God," Isaiah said. "I can't

find Him here. The air of Jerusalem is foul with men's evil ways. Let me go in peace, Father."

Amoz bowed his head. "I can't find the way for you. Go, my son. But I will tell you this. Jerusalem is your heart and you can't live long away from here. If you must, go in peace with my blessing."

And then Isaiah cried out, for he was gazing right at the Holy of Holies.

Chapter 5

In the weeks and months and years that passed, Isaiah was to recall his father's words. He learned much, living with the Rechabites. But he learned that the peace he thought was here in the quiet of the desert was not a true peace. There was the night that he and Noam had come across a jackal who had attacked a young kid, and they drove the jackal off with sticks and stones. Then the very next night, they found the jackal dead, a black festering wound in his side, where it had been bitten by a serpent.

"Animal fights animal as man fights man," Isaiah told the Prophetess, as he had named her, that night. "There is no peace anywhere. I was a fool to have run away. There is no escape. It's my responsibility to return."

"It's time," she said. "Don't feel bad."

"I'm not discouraged," Isaiah said. "I know there will come a time when the *spirit of wisdom and understanding* will prevail in our land, and then *the wolf shall dwell with the lamb, and the leopard shall lie down with the kid.*"

"You can do nothing here," she said. "Go in peace with my blessing."

Isaiah remembered his father's parting words to him and his heart ached with longing for his father and his home. When he had left Jerusalem so long ago, he had not been sure he loved this simple Rechabite girl. Now he knew. He would go back and tell his father and this time he would make his father understand.

"It will take me a few weeks to put my affairs in order in Jerusalem," Isaiah said. "But within a month, I will ask Noam to bring you to me."

"Isaiah, are you sure? I don't know anything of my family. I can come to you with no dowry."

"Do you call riches of the mind—no dowry? Don't your eyes shine brighter than diamonds?"

She laughed gaily. "You will have me believing your flattery, even believing—" She paused, her eyes lowering.

"Even that I love you. Yes, my Prophetess, I do love you and I want you to come to Jerusalem and be my wife."

But Isaiah's happy thoughts of a wedding were quickly dispelled when he entered Jerusalem. He found a funeral procession wending its way from the royal palace. He stood gaping, hardly able to talk as he glanced at the pallbearers. There was Daniel and Eben and Yuval. He clutched his heart as if he had been stabbed. "Jotham—could it be the King?" He turned to the nearest bystander.

"I have been away from the city," he said. "Who has died?"

The man looked at him curiously. "The news has traveled

far. Certainly you should have heard. King Uzziah, the leper."

Isaiah turned with a cry from the funeral crowd and fled down the streets, running until he was breathless. He got a stitch in his side and paused for a moment. No one would be at home. His father would be—he shook his head, as if to clear his thoughts. His father should have been a pall-bearer. He had been so close to the King; yet he hadn't seen him there. Where could he have been? Surely not at home, unless he were sick, so sick that he couldn't attend. Isaiah flew the rest of the way home. He burst into the house, his hair blown wildly, his eyes bright as if burning with fever, his cloak twisted as if tossed about in a storm.

His Aunt Reba staggered back when she saw him, as if she had seen a ghost. "You have heard," she said, and she covered her face with her hands and burst into tears.

"Yes, Uzziah is dead, a part of Judah is dead," he said.

She gulped back her tears, a sob strangling in her throat. "What words do you have to say for your father?" she flared out. "Where is your pity for him?"

"Reba, Reba," he put out his hand to keep himself from falling, "where's my father? Isn't he here?"

She shook her head. "I'm sorry. I thought you knew and that's why you had come back. Your father died last month."

"Last month!" Isaiah reeled back. "Couldn't you send someone to find me, couldn't you—"

"Obed tried. He was leaving for the north but he went out of his way. It seemed that you had left the last place where you were staying."

"Yes," Isaiah recalled. "I found that the well was contaminated. Several of the children got sick and we decided to move on." He turned to his aunt. "Will he ever forgive me for leaving him the way I did? How will he ever know of the deep love I had for him? How can I tell him now how grateful I am for all he did for me?"

"Isaiah, do you think he could have let you go if he didn't love you too much to hold you back? And don't think he didn't know of your feeling for him. He knew, though, that you had a greater love, and he wouldn't stand in your way."

"You don't mean the Rechabite girl?" Isaiah said. "I do love her and I want to marry her, but I left Jerusalem because I needed to find out if I was mouthing a lot of nonsense or if there might be hope of reaching the people, if the haughtiness of men might be brought low. I wanted to find peace. Where will I find it now?"

Before his aunt could stop him, Isaiah had staggered out of the house and was halfway up the road. Blindly, he let his feet carry him like a donkey free to roam at will, and all at once the ground under him felt familiar. He knew that he was on the road leading to the Temple.

As he dragged himself up the steps to the Temple, he knew that he was home—home at last. The peace that he had sought in the desert among the Rechabites was false. There was only one peace—the peace that comes from a knowledge of God.

As Isaiah climbed the steps to the Temple, he was surprised to see how deathly quiet it was. There were no beggars sitting on the steps crying for alms. He hurried forward. If only he could talk to Uriah. But of course, Uriah and all the priests would be at the funeral.

Funeral! His head spun. Whom had he come to mourn here—his father, his uncle Uzziah, or his own death, for now he felt as if he no longer moved of his own free will, but was a stranger even to himself.

The unrelenting sun beat down on the white limestone Temple walls. Isaiah leaned wearily against one of the burnished bronze entrance pillars. He pulled his hand back as if it had been scorched. The sun had made the bronze feel like molten lead.

He moved forward now and his pace quickened. He took a deep breath. Here in the soft gentle shadows of the *Hekhal*, he would find solace. A shaft of sunlight came down through the latticed windows, high up in the side walls. It fell on the altar of gold reserved for offerings of incense, which still glowed with coals from a recent sacrifice. Another shaft of light glimmered on the *Menorah*, whose seven wicks gave off their own burning light.

The Holy Place seemed bathed in gold, blazing with a strange fire. The shadows that Isaiah had first seen—or had he only believed them to be there?—had disappeared in this blinding light.

Another broad stream of light fell on the golden table, ten handbreadths long and five wide, on which was laid the twelve loaves of showbread.

Isaiah rubbed his eyes to try to clear away the blur but as he drew his palms away, he found that his hands were wet. Was it the unusual heat, he wondered, or were those tears that he had shed unknowingly?

He lifted his eyes to the Holy of Holies and another directing beam of light fell across the curtains that separated the Holy of Holies from the sanctuary.

And then Isaiah cried out, for he was gazing right at the Holy of Holies. Isaiah flung his hands over his eyes. No one but the High Priest was allowed to enter this inner sanctuary and then only on Yom Kippur, the Day of Atonement. What had he done? Was he to be punished for having left his father to die alone, without his only son at his side?

Isaiah backed away. He stumbled and threw out his hands to keep himself from falling. As he did so, he *"saw the Lord sitting upon a throne and His train filled the temple."* Isaiah moved no more. *"Above Him stood the seraphim."*

"They move, they are moving," Isaiah said. "It was no vision I had long ago. They are truly moving." While Isaiah stood rooted, the seraphim, each of which had six wings, flew towards Isaiah and as they beat the air with their wings, they called to one another,

"Holy, holy, holy, is the Lord of Hosts;
The whole earth is full of His glory."

Suddenly, all the blazing, golden glitter in the Holy of Holies seemed to vanish like a quickly melting fog and the sanctuary was filled with the smoke from the incense altar.

Isaiah put his hands to his head as if he felt it would burst. "I have sinned," he cried out.

"Woe is me, for I am undone;
Because I am a man of unclean lips,
And I dwell in the midst of a people of unclean lips;
For mine eyes have seen the King,
The Lord of Hosts."

He rocked back and forth in his grief like an old woman mourning the loss of a loved one.

Then one of the seraphim flew to Isaiah with a glowing stone in its hand, which it had taken from the altar with the tongs. It touched Isaiah's mouth with it.

"Lo, this hath touched thy lips;
And thine iniquity is taken away,
And thy sin expiated."

Isaiah lifted his head. He felt as if liquid silver were flowing through his body. He heard the voice of the Lord, saying:

"Whom shall I send,

And who will go for us?"

Isaiah's voice lifted, clear and bold, ringing into every corner of the Holy of Holies. "I will do your bidding. *Here am I. Send me."*

As he listened to the reply, each word cut into his heart. Isaiah felt himself sinking down lower and lower, for the Lord said:

"Go, and tell this people:
Hear ye indeed, but understand not;
And see ye indeed, but perceive not.
Make the heart of this people fat,
And make their ears heavy,
And shut their eyes;
Lest they, seeing with their eyes,
And hearing with their ears,
And understanding with their heart,
Return, and be healed."

"Lord, how long?" Isaiah asked wonderingly.

Isaiah shuddered with a chill, for the Lord answered,

"Until cities be waste without inhabitant,
And houses without man,
And the land become utterly waste,
And the Lord have removed men far away,
And the forsaken places be many in the midst of the
   land."

Isaiah ran out of the Temple as if pursued by demons. How could he deliver this message to his people? They had sinned but how could he tell them that Judah was to be destroyed? Would they know that they were not his words but the Lord's he was speaking?

Suddenly, he felt someone tugging at his hand, the way his father used to do. He turned and gazed into the face of Jacob, the fruit vendor.

"Are you ill, Isaiah?" he asked.

Isaiah put his hand to his lips. Would his lips be scorched from the coal? No, it felt as before. "I'm not ill but I have seen something—something—"

Jacob took his hand and gently they sat down on the Temple steps side by side. Isaiah looked around and saw that the beggars were beginning to trickle back. A few of the priests had already passed him by.

"It's over," Jacob said.

Isaiah turned to Jacob. "Listen to me, Jacob. It's not over. It's beginning. The Lord has sent me to be his messenger. From now on I will speak the Lord's words, even though they be bitter."

Jacob looked at him curiously. "Could you also be a spokesman for us without homes, without bread, and even without any chance to work for it?"

"I dare not voice what my mind suspects. Is it true about you?"

"Yes, the princes have taken my orchards. I would leave Jerusalem but I love it. I was born here. I will die here, in sight of the Temple."

There was a sudden commotion. "Clear the way," the beggars called out. "Ahaz, son of King Jotham, is coming."

Isaiah felt that this was a good omen. If Jotham's days were numbered, Ahaz would soon be the king. If he could only reach him. He knew of him as a thoughtless, pleasure-loving lad but if he could tell him the words of the Lord—

In a moment, Ahaz was before him, staring at him, as if he didn't recognize him. "Get out of my way, beggar," Ahaz roared, raising his hand to strike Isaiah. "Don't you recognize royal blood when you see it?"

It was then that Isaiah became conscious of his disheveled

appearance and tattered cloak. "Don't you recognize your brother?" Isaiah asked, lifting his head.

"Isaiah!" Eliakim, who had come with Ahaz and several other courtiers, rushed forward.

"I would never have believed it," Ahaz said. "You are greatly changed. You look different. There seems to be a glow about you." He teasingly prodded Isaiah with a stick he had picked up. "Go home and clean up, then you can join us. This funeral has depressed everybody. Zaccheus has invited a few of us to his home for a drink. We can't go to the palace because my father has fainted from the exertion of the funeral."

"Woe unto them that are mighty to drink wine,
And men of strength to mingle strong drink;
That justify the wicked for a reward,
And take away the righteousness of the righteous from
*   him!"*

"Hey, there, Isaiah, hold on," Zaccheus laughed. "I can remember lots of parties where you did your share of drinking."

"Yes," Josiah, another of the younger courtiers, grumbled. "If you don't want to join us—and come to think of it, who would want you in your present condition—you don't have to lecture us. We know what's right and what's wrong."

Isaiah lifted his hand.

"Woe unto them that call evil good,
And good evil;
That change darkness into light,
And light into darkness;
That change bitter into sweet,
And sweet into bitter!"

"It seems to me as if you are already drunk," Ahaz taunted. "You rave on as if wine had loosened your tongue."

"The Lord has freed my tongue," Isaiah said. "I'm not speaking for myself now. I am warning you of the anger of the Lord against His people."

"You've always been a good one at words," Ahaz said. "Save your brilliance for the Court. My father will be pleased to hear you're back. It seems to me you timed your return well. I suppose you hope to gain some advantage at Court."

"I had no such thing in mind," Isaiah stormed.

"Good," Ahaz laughed, "because when I become King, I can assure you, I won't be interested in your preachments."

"I'm not preaching," Isaiah said, trying to hold back his growing temper, "I'm begging—*cease to do evil, learn to do good.*"

"But we are doing good," Zaccheus cut in. "We have come to make a sacrifice to the Lord. Isn't that proof of our good intentions?"

"You fool," Isaiah burst out, no longer able to contain himself, "The Lord is *full of the burnt-offerings of rams.*"

"Don't let the priests hear you say that," Josiah jeered.

"Don't you understand," Isaiah pleaded, "the Lord does not want you to appear before him in this way, to trample His courts? The Lord hates your offerings. They are an abomination to Him."

"Well, then," Samuel, another of the courtiers, said, "let's not waste any time here. As long as Isaiah says the Lord doesn't want any sacrifices, I suppose we can go on our way."

"Good idea," Ahaz said, starting off. "I only came because my father insisted."

"Wait a minute," Isaiah called after them, "The Lord says,

When ye spread forth your hands,
I will hide Mine eyes from you;

Yea, when ye make many prayers,
I will not hear."

"What are you trying to do, scare us?" Ahaz scoffed. "Who do you think you are—a prophet?"

"From your lips has come the truth," Jacob said, springing in front of Ahaz. "From now on, Isaiah will be our prophet, the prophet of the poor, of the oppressed."

"Get out of my way," Ahaz said, smacking Jacob across the face with the stick he carried. "The smell of the poor suffocates me." Abruptly, he turned away from the Temple followed by his entourage.

Only Eliakim remained behind. He now came to Isaiah's side.

Isaiah waved him away. "Join them," he said. "I see that it will cost me dear to speak God's word. They don't want to hear about anything but pleasure. How can I tell them that this city I love will be destroyed?"

"Would a just God destroy Jerusalem?" Eliakim asked.

"Just?" Isaiah thundered. "Who but a just God would have waited so long?"

"Is there to be no hope?"

"Yes," Isaiah's eyes glowed brightly. "A remnant will be saved."

Eliakim took Isaiah's hand. "Come, I will walk you home. Your aunt has long waited for you. She vowed she would not go to Israel and marry Obed until you returned."

"I must bring joy to the house once more, as it was in the days when my mother was alive." Isaiah turned to Eliakim excitedly. "As soon as it is possible, I'll marry the Rechabite girl. It's not seemly to think of life and joy when death is so close at hand, but that is one of life's burdens—the need to go on in spite of everything."

Isaiah raised his arms heavenward. . . .

Chapter 6

Isaiah's marriage to the Rechabite girl did bring much joy into his home and their happiness was doubled when a year later, in 739 B.C.E., he was blessed with a son, Shear-jashub. Isaiah was pleased that at the palace, too, Ahaz was celebrating the birth of a son, Hezekiah. Perhaps, at last, the birth of a child would make Ahaz realize his new responsibilities. Jotham had passed away and, fearfully, Isaiah watched Ahaz come to power. He had told his wife of his concern. "Now that Ahaz is King, it will be sad for my people. A *babe is their master, and women rule over them.*"

"Give him a chance," his wife encouraged. "Now that he's faced with the Kingship, he may change."

But this proved a vain hope and Isaiah worried about the fate of Judah. Conditions abroad were in turmoil and year by year they grew worse. He had lately received disturbing news from Obed about the troubled state of affairs in northern Israel. Menahem had died and his son, who succeeded him, was murdered soon after. Pekah, the regicide, now ruled as King.

Although Isaiah was in the King's Council, Ahaz was not open to sharing affairs of state with him. To his dismay, Shebna had been placed at the head of the government and Isaiah found that he was absenting himself more and more from the councilors' meetings.

Therefore, he was surprised one morning when Eliakim, Daniel and Josiah came to him in great distress.

"Some ambassadors have recently arrived from Pekah and Rezin in Syria. They have presented themselves several times at Court, but Ahaz has been too busy with banquets and feasts to see them. They are growing impatient," Eliakim explained.

"Impatient!" Daniel cut in. "They are on the verge of leaving. They refuse to speak to us, but Isaiah, I know they will talk to you. You have great influence and your reputation has spread far and wide."

"Why should I interfere?" Isaiah said. "Anything I may advise will only be contradicted by Shebna. He bears no love for my country. He's only using his position to fatten his purse."

"You have never borne any man ill will," Eliakim said. "Forget Shebna and think of Judah."

"All right," Isaiah agreed. "I'll meet with the ambassadors."

But it was already too late. Angered by Ahaz's undignified reception and neglect of them, they had left. "Perhaps Shebna knows the purpose of their mission," Daniel said. "He has spies everywhere."

"Will you see him, Isaiah?" Eliakim asked.

"If you wish."

Shebna laughed insolently, when Isaiah explained that he and his friends had been disturbed by the sudden departure of the ambassadors. "It's of small matter," Shebna said loftily. "They want us to do them a favor so it won't hurt them to beg and grovel a bit longer."

"You can't treat nations the way you treat men," Isaiah said.

Shebna's black eyes narrowed. "I seek no help from you in affairs of state, Isaiah. Rezin and Pekah have joined in a league to defy Assyria and nothing could suit me better. The ambassadors want us to join with them so that we can all break our vassalage to Assyria."

"Surely you would not think of doing this," Isaiah said.

"Why not?" Shebna retorted. "Tiglath-Pileser is busy fighting in the Far East. He will be well occupied for some time. All we need do is to join with these others—"

"No, no, Shebna," Isaiah cried out. His father's words on their visit to Tiglath-Pileser returned to him. By herself Judah could survive. In a league with others, she would be threatened. "We should not join this league."

Shebna dismissed him curtly. "When Ahaz or I want your advice, we will ask for it."

But Isaiah was not to be set aside so lightly. That evening, he told his wife, "I'll be going on a few days' journey into the hills. I'll be back as soon as I find out for myself what is going on. I can't trust Shebna. He switches sides, for his own purposes. I can only trust my own ears."

"Where will you go?" his wife asked.

Isaiah smiled. "You should know. I'll seek out Noam. Together we should be able to gather the news that is carried like wind in the desert and hills but sometimes gets lost in the city."

In a few days, Isaiah returned with the news he had

wanted. Syria and Israel were ready to attack Judah. Their plan was to besiege Jerusalem and force its surrender.

Isaiah went directly to Ahaz with the news. "Their plan is very carefully worked out," Isaiah explained. "They are hoping to put a Syrian, the son of Tabeel, in your place as King."

"Why doesn't Shebna know of this?" Ahaz said. "Surely his sources of information are more reliable than yours. Perhaps," Ahaz ridiculed, "this is another of your fantastic dreams."

"When you hear the sound of battle on your doorstep, you will realize it's no dream."

In a few months, Ahaz found the battle on his doorstep. Syria and northern Israel had banded together and attacked Judah. Daniel and other men of high position had fallen in the first battles. Jerusalem was now caught in a state of siege. Panic spread through the Court and the city, like a plague sweeping the land.

In desperation, Zaccheus came to see Isaiah. "You are wise. What do you suggest we do to protect ourselves? I have jewels, land—"

"Yes," Isaiah said. "I understand that on the land of Jacob, the fruit vendor, you built a mansion that dazzles the eyes."

"That's of little moment now. How can I save myself and my family. You have a son. What are you going to do?"

"Do?" Isaiah spread out his hands. "I will sit still and wait."

"Wait for what? The Syrians will be pounding on our walls before you know it."

"The Lord will protect me," Isaiah said. "Why should I run from the protection of the Lord?"

Zaccheus shrugged. "I can see it's no good talking to you.

A Syrian's sword will draw blood from you as any other. If you wish to sit still and die, that's your affair. I came to you because I thought you might have heard some news of the messengers Ahaz sent to Tiglath-Pileser asking for help. Things are so confused at the palace that—"

"Ahaz has asked Tiglath-Pileser for help?" Isaiah repeated, horrified. "How could he? That's the worst thing that he could do. I've got to go to the palace and see Ahaz immediately."

"He's not there," Zaccheus said. "He and Shebna have gone to check the water supply at the conduit."

Isaiah stood up and turned to his wife. "Don't bother making the noonday meal for me. I may be delayed. I've got to see Ahaz at once."

"Father, may I please go with you?" Shear-jashub asked. "Maybe Hezekiah is with the King and I can play with him."

"No, no," Isaiah brushed the child away impatiently. "I'm too busy."

"Too busy for your own son?" his wife asked, accusingly.

"It's not that. You know it will not be easy convincing Ahaz of the right thing to do. Shear-jashub will only get in the way."

"It would be good for the child to get in the way," his wife suggested. "Have you forgotten your son's name means a *remnant shall return*. Perhaps Ahaz needs to be reminded."

Isaiah put out his hand and together, he and his young son set off. As they cut across the fuller's field, Isaiah saw a group of people clustered about, inspecting the crucial water supply. He hastened his steps, hardly realizing that he was pulling Shear-jashub along.

Shebna spotted Isaiah first and separated from the group. "This is a long way to go for an afternoon stroll. Haven't you heard the Syrians have captured Elath? Aren't you making plans to hide in the hills as so many brave people are doing?" he taunted.

"What other news is there?" Isaiah asked, stunned.

"The best news of all," Ahaz said, joining them. "Tiglath-Pileser is sending help to us."

"Don't you see that by turning to Tiglath-Pileser, you are turning us into a slave state," Isaiah said. "We're small. Our hills and mountains will protect us. We mean little to the great King of Assyria if we stay out of entangling alliances."

Ahaz waved Isaiah aside. "We have no time for your religious fervor now. You mean well. I know that; otherwise I would have lost my patience with you before this. But this is war. You are a man of peace. You don't understand these things."

"You must listen to the voice of the Lord," Isaiah said. "He bids me say unto you, *keep calm; fear not.*"

"Keep calm!" Ahaz burst out. "Do you know what you are saying?"

"Yes," Isaiah pressed on. "Your enemies are nothing but two tails of smoking firebrands. Before long, Damascus will be destroyed and Israel will cease to be a nation. The Lord has said it. If you have faith, it shall come to pass and Jerusalem will survive."

"I'm busy now," Ahaz said abruptly. "I'll do what I can to save Jerusalem in my own way. Look," he pointed, "your son trudges wearily at your side. Don't plague me. Don't plague him. It's hot. I'll go to the Temple after I have finished checking how the water will hold out. If you want to speak with me again, I'll meet you there."

"So be it," Isaiah said and started back for his home in the Middle City.

Suddenly aware that Shear-jashub had been at his side all this time, patiently, silently, Isaiah bent down and patted the young boy's head. "I didn't mean to forget you."

The boy looked at him with wide, serious eyes. "Will God save all of us?"

"No," Isaiah shook his head, "only a remnant will remain, a mere tenth. The others will fall away like dead branches on an oak. But the heart of the tree—the holy seed—will endure. You, my son, I hope will be chosen."

"And Hezekiah, too?" the little one asked quickly. "He's my friend."

"Yes, there's hope for Hezekiah, too," Isaiah said. "I must gather you together soon and teach you how to serve the true God, the one God." He put his arm around the boy's thin shoulders and recalled how many times his father had used the same fond gesture with him. "You don't understand my words. They must weary you, as they do the King. I'll take you to your mother, where you belong."

Shear-jashub bent down and picked up a rock from the field. He playfully tossed it into the air. As he caught it, it struck his finger a glancing blow and cut it.

"I'll find a fig leaf and wrap it around the finger," Isaiah said. "It will stop the blood at once."

"Are you sure?" Shear-jashub asked, sucking at the finger.

"Yes, a doctor whom my father befriended told me this and it has always worked." He clasped the boy's hand in his. "Some day you will meet him. The doctor is your Uncle Obed."

"I hope the wicked soldiers don't kill me," Shear-jashub said. "There are so many people I want to meet."

"I fear your mother's wrath more than any soldier, so let's hurry along. It's late."

Soon after Isaiah had returned home with his son and eaten a hasty repast, he was on his way to the Temple.

A huge crowd had gathered, for they had heard that the King was coming to make a sacrifice. In a short while, there was a shout as Ahaz and some of the courtiers came slowly up the Temple hill.

"The bright flame will soon glow from my sacrificial lamb," Ahaz said, stopping directly in front of Isaiah. "What more would you have me do?"

"*Hear the word of the Lord,*" Isaiah cried out.

"*Ye rulers of Sodom;*

Give ear unto the law of our God,

Ye people of Gomorrah.

To what purpose is the multitude of your sacrifices unto
Me?"

"If prayers are not enough, and sacrifices are not enough, tell me, Isaiah," Ahaz chided, "what does your God desire?"

"A simple thing." The crowd pressed closer." *Come now,* says the Lord, *and let us reason together.*" Isaiah opened his arms wide.

"*Though your sins be as scarlet,*

They shall be as white as snow;

Though they be red like crimson,

They shall be as wool.

If ye be willing and obedient,

Ye shall eat the good of the land;

But if ye refuse and rebel,

Ye shall be devoured with the sword."

"We certainly will be devoured by the sword if we stay here any longer," Shebna intervened.

Isaiah's voice rose like the night wind out of the desert. "What do you say, Ahaz? Must another, a foreign-born, speak for you?" Isaiah whirled on Shebna. "What are you doing here so close to the Temple? What right do you have to call Judah your home?"

A murmur of agreement ran through the crowd. "The Prophet speaks true," a man close at hand said. "It's no secret. Shebna worships idols in his home. I have heard—"

"Shh!" a woman called out excitedly. "The Prophet speaks again!"

"If you won't listen to me, O King of Judah, *ask thee a sign of the Lord thy God: ask it either in the depth, or in the height above.*"

Ahaz hesitated. Was Isaiah's God so strong that he could turn the wrath of Syria and Israel from them? He turned to Shebna for guidance. The thin, small man moved closer to the King's side. He shook his head almost imperceptibly from side to side. Ahaz's irresolution disappeared. But he realized he would have to be wary. The throng would have to be appeased. The Prophet had many friends among the rabble. A sly smile crossed his face. "I will not ask for a sign. Surely you don't suggest that I doubt the word of the Lord. I will not test Him."

Isaiah raised his arms heavenward so that he looked like a firmly rooted tree with its branches stretching up. "Hear ye now, O House of David, isn't it enough that you weary the people with your oily tongue, will you weary my God also?"

Shebna stepped forward. "How dare you talk to the King in this way?"

"Step back," Isaiah thundered and his eyes rolled like flashes of summer lightning. "The Lord himself will give you a sign." He pointed his finger into the milling, breathless crowd. "Behold a young woman—you—" and a woman drew back gasping, "shall bear a son and shall name him Immanuel. Before he is old enough to know the difference between good and evil, before three or four years have passed, Rezin and Pekah shall be no more."

Uriah, the priest, who was standing close by, said, "If only your words could be branded across the sky. The King hears but does not hear."

Isaiah suddenly turned and called out to Zechariah, the son of Jeberechiah, who was passing by, "Come with me, my friend, and you, too, Uriah, if you have the time. I want you to be faithful witnesses to what I record. There's nothing more that I can do here."

Majestically, Isaiah strode off. The tread of his sandals was the only sound he left behind him.

Isaiah walked swiftly with Zechariah and Uriah trailing behind him. Isaiah burst into his house calling out, "My wife, please fetch me my pen."

His wife quickly brought him a sheet of papyrus and a pen made of a reed with soft fibers at one end. Isaiah took a knife and trimmed the end of his pen, then he paused, his head lifted as if someone were calling to him. He pushed the papyrus aside. "The Lord has said unto me, *Take thee a great tablet and write upon it in common script—*"

Zechariah and Uriah came through the doorway at that moment, panting and breathless.

"We can't be a witness to what we don't see," Zechariah laughed. "You walked as if you had wings."

"Forgive me," Isaiah said. "I didn't mean to be impolite."

"What can we do to help you?" Uriah asked. "Your words on the Temple steps still ring in my ears."

"Find me a large tablet, if you are able," Isaiah said, "and I will set it up as a sign on the roof top of my house so that all may see and read it."

"What will you put on it?" Shear-jashub asked coming forward.

Isaiah tousled the little one's hair. "Watch me," he said, "and you will see."

A short while later, Uriah came in, lugging an enormous wooden tablet. All gathered round Isaiah.

Slowly he sketched, *"Maher."*

"Maher, maher," Shear-jashub said slowly, rolling the word around in his mouth, as if he were tasting it. Suddenly his face brightened. "It means haste."

"Good for you," Isaiah said, absorbed in finishing the next word: *Shalal.* He glanced at his son. "Is that too difficult for you?"

Shear-jashub nodded. Isaiah glanced up. "The booty," Zechariah murmured under his breath.

"But what does it mean?" Shear-jashub asked impatiently.

"Wait a bit. I'm not finished," Isaiah said and added on the tablet, *"Hash"* and *"baz."*

"Speed the prey," Uriah said gently, as if saying a prayer, "The spoil speedeth, the prey hasteth."

"Will the people understand?" Zechariah asked. "Will the people know that peace is our only solution—peace through God's path of righteousness? Will they realize that Assyria will kill us by strangling and Damascus will kill us by the sword? It's death for us either way. Will the people see that your way is the only right way?"

"They will see the sign," Isaiah said. "They will stop and look. They'll talk. That's all I ask." He gazed fondly at his wife. "And you, my beloved, next year, you will bear a son and his name shall be Maher-shalal-hash-baz, and before he knows how to say my father and my mother, the riches of Damascus and the spoils of Samaria shall be carried away before the King of Assyria."

"I am Sarah, widow of Jonathan."

Chapter 71

Season followed season and death followed life. Isaiah's wife died in giving birth to Maher-shalal-hash-baz. The night that he had put his wife to eternal rest, Isaiah found himself wandering aimlessly beside the softly flowing waters of Shiloah. There, dry-eyed, he stood mourning his loss.

"Bring me the relief of tears, O Lord," he cried aloud, but his grief was knotted in his heart and the tears would not come.

As he stood in the shadows, he heard the muffled sound of weeping. He approached slowly and discovered a woman, huddled over, at the banks of the river.

"Woman, what are you doing out at this hour of the night?" he asked gently.

"My dark thoughts pull me to the darkness of the night," she said.

"A grief that is shared is cut in two," Isaiah said, feeling that here was one who had been called out by the night as he had been, because of deep sorrow. "Tell me what's wrong, and I'll listen."

"Listen?" she wailed, covering her face with her robe. "Who listens to the widow? Who listens to the plaint of the fatherless? My son has just joined an Israelite caravan. I'll never see him again. He was only ten but what could I do? I'm alone in the world. I didn't know where to get food and my house—my poor wretched house—the princes are taking it."

Isaiah clenched his hands in fury. "What's your name?" He knelt down beside her.

"I am Sarah, widow of Jonathan."

"I'm not acquainted with you," Isaiah said.

She looked at his handsome face, at the fine cloth of his robe, and her eyes flared with sudden anger. "Why should you know me? You are one of them. You are a noble."

"I am one with God," Isaiah said.

"Why should you care if another widow is left to starve in the streets?" she went on bitterly.

"I care because God cares. He says we should seek justice, relieve the oppressed, plead for the widow."

"You do not sound like—" she faltered.

"The ways of God are strange," Isaiah said slowly. "By sharing my grief with you, perhaps like the waters of Shiloah, it will flow away." He put out his hand entreatingly. "Sarah, would you be a nurse to my newborn son? Would you be more than a nurse? Would you be his second mother?"

"Do you speak to me out of pity? Do you wish to take me into your home because you feel sorry for me?"

"Sarah, my good woman, is pity a vice to be scorned? Accept my pity. I offer you the security and protection of my home. I welcome you into my family. Come with me now."

She drew back. "Wouldn't people think it strange for you to take a woman into your house at this time?"

"All who know me know that there will be no other wife for me in this world other than the one I have had." At the thought of his wife, his hands trembled. He touched his face and felt the welcome relief of tears at last. "We were bound together by more than one spirit, one heart, one flesh. We thought as one."

"I don't know," Sarah hesitated. "You are kind, too kind to take me into your home so willingly. You don't know anything about me. Perhaps you should first—"

"Sarah, you are a woman, with a mother's heart that has just been torn. I tell you one day your boy will return. Until then, be a mother to my children. No man can take a mother's place. I loved my father. He was a kind man, a great man. But when I was sick or troubled, I called out in my distress, 'Oh, my mother, help me.' I did not call to my father." His voice cracked on the tears of his sorrow and it was some minutes before he could go on. "My oldest son, Shear-jashub, is growing up, like the wild grass in the hills, much too fast. I can guide him but there will be times when he will need a gentle hand to soothe his fevered brow. There will be times when he will want a woman's advice and soft words. Let us dry our tears together, Sarah. Let me help you that I may help myself."

Sarah stood up. She took Isaiah's hand and clasped it in her own. "The darkness hides your face but your words do not hide the goodness in your heart. I'll go with you."

And so Sarah, widow of Jonathan, came to Isaiah's house. As the days passed, Shear-jashub found her a source of comfort for Isaiah was still too tied up in his mourning to help his son. And Maher-shalal-hash-baz loved her for he knew no other mother.

The days passed but Isaiah's grief did not.

One morning, Uriah and Eliakim came to Isaiah to see what they could do. Uriah argued that the period of mourning had passed and that God did not look favorably upon excessive grief. "You must consider your son," Uriah urged. "You must *sanctify his name.*"

"I have been to the Temple," Isaiah said.

"You must do more," Uriah insisted. "For the sake of Judah, for whom your son's name is to serve as a warning, you must have an official ceremony to celebrate the naming of your child."

"There's much fear in our land," Eliakim plunged in. "Assyria is crushing one country after another under its yoke. It's like a wind that can't be stopped."

"The man who fears God need fear no man," Isaiah said. "Do you think that Assyria is unconquerable? Is her king more clever than other men?" He shook his head. "Eliakim, what is happening is allowed to transpire because God wills it so, not man. God has His own plan." Isaiah went to a table and handed Eliakim a sheet of paper. "Read," he urged, handing it to him. "Do you think my private grief is so great that I cannot mourn for my country, too?"

Eliakim took the paper. Uriah moved closer, peering over Eliakim's shoulder. Eliakim began reading aloud:

"Is the plowman never done with plowing to sow,
With the opening and harrowing of his ground?
When he hath made plain the face thereof,
Doth he not cast abroad the black cummin, and scatter
the cummin,
And put in the wheat in rows and the barley in the
appointed place
And the spelt in the border thereof?

For He doth instruct him aright;
His God doth teach him."

Eliakim paused, rereading the lines again silently. "How well you put it, Isaiah, that God has His own carefully thought out way of doing things. The farmer must plow before he sows. If this is true, then God who teaches the farmer, must also plow the divine fields according to plan."

Isaiah nodded. "Go on. See what you think of the rest."

Uriah took the sheet from Eliakim's hands. "Please," he said, "my eyes are not as good as yours. I don't want to miss a word." Stroking his beard, he mumbled under his breath,

"For the black cummin is not threshed with a threshing-
sledge,
Neither is a cart-wheel turned about upon the cummin;
But the black cummin is beaten out with a staff,
And the cummin with a rod."

He drew the paper closer to him, squinting at it hard. "Here," he pointed to a line, "Isaiah, I'm sorry I can't quite make this out. What does it say exactly?"

"Is bread corn crushed?" Isaiah said, closing his eyes, the lines vivid in his memory.

"Nay, he will not ever be threshing it;
And though the roller of his wagon and its sharp edges
move noisily,
He doth not crush it.
This also cometh forth from the Lord of Hosts;
Wonderful is His counsel, and great His wisdom."

"Let me take this to a scribe," Uriah said excitedly. "I would like to have a copy made. I want the priests in the Temple to hear it."

"I would like those at Court to hear it, too," Eliakim broke in.

"Hold on," Uriah said. "We are forgetting ourselves. I came here today with another purpose." He looked steadily at Isaiah. "When will we proclaim your son's name throughout the land?"

A silence hung over the house, like that split-second moment between light and darkness when the sun finally sinks to rest. "By week's end," Isaiah said. "Sarah will need time to prepare."

Uriah rolled up the sheet of paper with the verse on it and put it in the folds of his cloak. He stepped forward and embraced Isaiah. "My son, we need you. May your joy now be as strong as your grief."

By week's end, the house was shining with a new light. Isaiah's heart had lifted and those about him worked eagerly and happily. Sarah and the cook had baked and baked until the cakes were piled high on the silver trays; the countryside had been scoured for the best and plumpest fruits in season, and the wine decanters were full.

There was hurrying and scurrying and much fussing about Maher-shalal-hash-baz's swaddling clothes and then before they knew it, there was a shadow in the doorway and unthinkingly Sarah cried out, "It's so early. We had not expected—"

A young boy came forward timidly, holding out a gift. "I am Jeremy, son of Obadiah. I have a gift for the babe."

"Thank you," Sarah said kindly. "It's not time yet for the feast but make yourself welcome."

He glanced around. "I—I—forgive me," he stammered. "I came early by intention. I had hoped that I might have a word with the Prophet. I heard him speak at the Temple, the day he told of Immanuel, and I have not been able to sleep since."

Sarah smiled. Ah, that worshipful light in the young boy's eyes!

"I will call Isaiah," she said. "I'm sure—"

But even as she spoke, Isaiah came in. "I heard voices," he said. "I thought perhaps the time had flown quicker than I realized and guests were beginning to arrive." He looked at the youngster. "Who are you, my son?"

"Jeremy, son of Obadiah. I—I—" His lips trembled and he could not go on.

"He brought a gift for the child," Sarah said gently. "He wanted a word with you," and she quietly withdrew.

Isaiah put out his hand. "Come, let's go to the roof top," he said. "We may catch a stray breeze. There's always time to speak to such as you."

Jeremy lifted his head and his clear, shining eyes sought Isaiah's. "The remnant," Isaiah murmured to himself. "Yes, we will yet be saved."

"There's so much I want to know," Jeremy said.

"And so much I want to tell," Isaiah answered. "You may have pointed the way for me. If I cannot reason with the elders at Court, perhaps I should start with the youngsters in the streets." Isaiah leaned forward, his eyes ablaze. "My battle is greater than the battle being waged outside our city walls. How can I fight the idols in our land? How can I gather strength to struggle against the stupidity in men that splinters the one God into fragments, one for this nation, and one for this and—"

"Let me stand by your side," Jeremy cried out. "I'll do your bidding."

Isaiah patted the boy's head. "No, do the Lord's bidding and we'll both be satisfied."

Isaiah stood up. "I hear the sound of much noise. The guests must be arriving. Let's go below."

When they got downstairs, they found that King Ahaz, Shebna and several nobles had just arrived.

"Despite the precarious state of our nation's affairs," Ahaz said, as Isaiah came forward to greet him, "I felt it would be remiss if I did not share in your joy."

"Your hour of triumph is coming, too," Isaiah said. "Soon you will receive the news that Damascus is a *ruinous heap* and that all our enemies have been blown away like dust."

"I don't want to contradict our good host," Shebna interrupted, "but there's not one nation in Palestine and along the Mediterranean that has not united together against Assyria. Why should we hold back from joining with so many? Can they all be wrong and you right?"

"*Ah, the uproar of many peoples,*" Isaiah answered,
"*That roar like the roaring of the seas;*
And the rushing of nations, that rush
Like the rushing of mighty waters.
He shall rebuke them, and they shall flee far off,
And shall be chased as the chaff of the mountains before
the wind,
And like the whirling dust before the storm."

He smiled. "By morning they will be gone."

"This foolishness is for children," Shebna scoffed. "Teach it to Hezekiah, who I have heard mouthing your nonsense in the halls of the palace."

"I teach him the truth," Isaiah said. "It's the hearer who must have a sharp ear, not just a sharp wit, to recognize the difference between truth and falsehood. Woe to those who turn things upside down and make evil into good."

Shebna sidled up close to the King. "Listen well," he said

in an undertone. "Perhaps it would be better not to expose Hezekiah to such talk. He comes here much too freely. One day he will be King."

Ahaz turned to see Hezekiah and Shear-jashub playing and laughing together in a corner of the room. "Shear-jashub is a good friend of his. No, I can't take him away. Isaiah is not his only teacher. He will learn," he laughed, "by my precept—and yours as well."

In a short while, the King prepared to leave. As the entourage was about to depart, a spy whom Shebna had sent out, burst in on the assemblage. "Pekah has been defeated and slain," the messenger gasped. "Forgive me for breaking in on you this way but when I didn't find you at the palace—"

"You did right," Ahaz said. "Your news is most important."

"What else have you learned?" Shebna asked.

"Tiglath-Pileser has set up Hoshea to take Pekah's place. It's said that Hoshea grovels in the ground like a worm before the might of Assyria."

"Oh, woe, woe is Israel!" Isaiah lamented.

"Woe!" Shebna turned on him. "You are a patriot. You should rejoice at this news."

"I wish that I could," Isaiah said. "But my heart bleeds for her people."

"The wails of the captives split the heavens," the messenger continued. "Tiglath-Pileser has taken thousands of the Israelites and is dispersing them throughout the various lands of his empire."

"Good," Ahaz said delightedly. "This is an event to celebrate."

Isaiah stopped the King in the doorway. "This is not Assyria's doing, but God's. Do you see that the Lord has spoken true? And soon Damascus shall cease to be."

Isaiah's prediction came true. Rezin was slain and Damascus taken.

After the fall of Damascus, Tiglath-Pileser ordered a great *Durbar* to celebrate his victory. He commanded all the tributary kings in Palestine to pay homage to him there. To Damascus came the Kings of Edom, of Moab; and Hanno, who was leader of the Philistine cities, and Ahaz. To Isaiah's dismay, Ahaz went to Damascus gladly, bearing tribute with no sense of shame. The reports of Ahaz's fascination with the foreign fashions and customs trickled back to Jerusalem. Month after month passed and Ahaz sought excuses to delay his return to Jerusalem.

One afternoon Uriah came to Isaiah with the news that Ahaz had sent Urijah, the high priest in Jerusalem, instructions to make the same kind of altar as the one used by Tiglath-Pileser when he offered sacrifices to Ashur, the Assyrian god.

"Ahaz says in his letter that Tiglath-Pileser always carries this altar with him," Uriah said, "and since it has brought the Assyrians such great victories, it would not hurt for us to try it."

Isaiah couldn't hide his concern. "I remember what happened when King Uzziah tried to take over the priestly office, and my heart is full of dread."

"If only Urijah were like Azariah!" Uriah said. "But he's not. He'll do whatever Ahaz says."

"All priests are not wise," Isaiah said. "They can be blinded by the glitter of gifts and gold."

"Who knows what other strange notions Ahaz will carry back with him?" Uriah shrugged. "His letter tells of a huge

Damascene sundial which he plans to set up in the palace courtyard so that the people may come from miles around to see it. My stomach turns sour when I think of—" he stopped, for Hezekiah had just entered.

"I came as quickly as I could. Isaiah, I want you to know that if I were King, the altar would not be built," Hezekiah burst out. "You have taught me that it is idolatry."

"There's much time yet before the reins of government fall happily into your hands," Isaiah said.

But the time was to come much sooner than they thought.

When Ahaz finally returned from Damascus, there was much unrest. The people felt ashamed at how willingly Ahaz went and humbled himself before the Assyrian king. They were appalled at the luxuries and foreign styles which he adopted.

"The people don't want you for their King," Shebna warned. "My men report that the people feel you are not acting like a King. The grumbles of complaint are becoming mighty roars."

"I don't want to be King," Ahaz said petulantly. "It's tiresome. You know the temper of my people. Foreign-born though you are, you have adopted my land as your own. What would you advise?"

"A fine plan," Shebna smiled. "You will be King and yet not King."

Ahaz laughed. "And how will we master this trick?"

"Make your son co-ruler with you. The people love Hezekiah. Give him the onerous jobs, the troubling affairs of state." Shebna's eyes narrowed craftily. "It will help to keep him out of Isaiah's clutches. Occupy the boy's time with national problems. Keep him busy and you'll keep him away from Isaiah."

"An admirable idea!" Ahaz approved heartily. "But won't the people say he's too young?"

"So much the better," Shebna said. "They will forgive his mistakes or," he laughed, "they will blame them on Isaiah."

The Courtiers gasped. "How dare you tell the
king that he's to die?"

Chapter 8 /

When Hezekiah became King, it was as if a veil had been pulled away from the face of Judah. The country blossomed forth under the golden blessings of peace and prosperity.

"The glories of Solomon and the greatness of Uzziah will bear fruit under Hezekiah," Isaiah told Jeremy and the small group of followers who had come together for instruction from Isaiah.

The ringing sound of the ax in the desert as forty-six fortresses were built to protect Jerusalem, the thud and scrape of the plow as it cut into fields long unused, gave strength to Isaiah's words. During the time that he ruled jointly with his father, Hezekiah listened to the voice of his teacher. Each day's events were discussed with Isaiah. The world became his copybook. Isaiah taught Hezekiah to keep his eyes not on Judah alone but on nations far beyond. So smoothly did he rule that there was hardly any disturbance on Ahaz's death. But there were some changes in the palace rule. Eliakim was put in charge of affairs of state and Shebna was shunted off to a minor position. Out of loyalty to his father, Hezekiah felt he could not dismiss Shebna completely from the country's affairs.

Changes in government were taking place elsewhere. Tiglath-Pileser had been succeeded by Shalmaneser V. Once more there were rumbles of revolt among the tributary nations. Shebna found many occasions to get Hezekiah's ear and urge that Hezekiah join Egypt and other Palestinian countries in an attempt to overthrow Shalmaneser. But though Shebna could gain Hezekiah's ear, it was Isaiah who had entrance to his heart, and so Hezekiah remained out of the alliances that formed and re-formed like the shifting sands in the desert.

Never did Judah bring forth such an abundant harvest. The olive crop was the biggest in years and the grapes the sweetest. But it was Isaiah's greatness of heart that yielded the finest crop. No one was too small to win his attention; no task was too big for him to undertake. He was able to get Jacob, the beggar, a farm of his own. Through his influence, Hezekiah bestowed lavish gifts upon the Temple and the pillars were overlaid with gold. But it was not this show of wealth that pleased Isaiah. It was the glitter of a new light, the dawn of a reborn religious fervor that swept through the country. The Temple was purified, idols destroyed and the "high places" where many people offered sacrifices to strange gods were trampled down.

Just as Judah thrived under Isaiah's guidance, so his sons grew to manhood, warm in the circle of his love. He was proud of the way his sons were welcomed at the palace and he was pleased to hear their voices lifted in thoughtful debate on national policies. At times he was disturbed by Maher-shalal-hash-baz's self-indulgence, but he realized that Sarah had spoiled him and perhaps he himself was to blame for not having taken a stronger stand with him.

Isaiah was distressed therefore when Maher-shalal-hash-baz came to him one afternoon with the news that Shebna had been sent on a special mission to Merodachbaladan, King of Babylon.

Isaiah had been too busy lately to go to the palace. A library had been set up and Isaiah had been advising and watching the scribes who were copying many ancient and revered manuscripts. Isaiah was thrilled as day by day he saw the words of Solomon, Amos, Micah and Hosea, and even his own poems, copied and preserved forever.

"Why shouldn't Shebna go?" Maher-shalal-hash-baz asked, quick to see Isaiah's displeasure. "The King would have sent you and we could have had a fine time, if you weren't so stubborn in your views. You should be proud that such a great king as Merodachbaladan wants to have anything to do with Judah."

"I would expect words like this from Shebna, not from my own son," Isaiah said, frowning.

"You can't ignore the fact that there are many at Court who side with Shebna. They think—"

"They do not think beyond their own self-interests," Isaiah snapped. "What other news is there?"

"The King had a fainting spell. It may be nothing—"

"Nothing!" Isaiah rose, his face darkening like a thundercloud. "If Hezekiah becomes sick now, all may be lost. We have just begun to do the many things that cry out for life. If someone else takes his place, everything that we have started may be crushed before it has a chance."

"Well, go see Hezekiah, and find out for yourself exactly what is going on."

But Isaiah was too upset by Shebna's mission to go see Hezekiah. Even as the days flew by and the news of Hezekiah's illness became a favorite topic in the market place, Isaiah stayed away.

Finally, it was Shear-jashub who prodded Isaiah. "You may be annoyed with Hezekiah as King but surely you have compassion for him as a man."

Isaiah bowed his head. "I feel ashamed that my own son should have to remind me of my duty. I'll go to the palace at once."

When Isaiah arrived and was led to the King's bedchamber, he was amazed to see how weak Hezekiah was. But Isaiah was even more disturbed by the blandishments and false hopes of the men around the King's bedside. He heard the courtiers fawningly pretend that Hezekiah would get well in no time.

The King finally turned to him and said, "Forgive me, *I do moan as a dove.* Too long have you been absent from this house, Isaiah. Too long has your voice been silent in my ear. Tell me, what do you think?"

Sternly Isaiah said, "Don't listen to this childish prattle. The Lord says, '*Set thy house in order; for thou shalt die, and not live.*'"

The courtiers gasped. "How dare you tell the King that he's to die?" Levi, son of Aaron, shouted, as Isaiah spun on his heel and started to leave.

"I have spoken the Lord's words. They are as bitter to me as they are to you," Isaiah countered, over his shoulder.

He paused for a moment, hearing Hezekiah writhing in agony. He watched Hezekiah turn his face to the wall and call out, "*Remember now, O Lord, I beseech Thee, how I have walked before Thee in truth and with a whole heart, and have done that which is good in Thy sight.*"

As the tears rolled down Hezekiah's cheeks, Isaiah could feel his own tears start, and quietly he withdrew.

Down the palace steps, through the courtyard, past the sundial which Ahaz had brought from Damascus, went Isaiah, and his steps faltered for his eyes were blinded with tears.

He loved Hezekiah as his own, and he had withheld the hand of friendship from him. He must go back at once and ask the King's forgiveness. He had been too hasty. If only there were some good word, some measure of hope that he could bring back with him. Isaiah stepped aside as some youngsters raced past him. "There's a caravan in from Babylon," they shouted. "Hurry, let's see what they are unloading at the city gate."

Isaiah closed his eyes for a moment, swaying as if he were about to faint. As a child, he had sat listening to remarkable tales of recovery told by doctors from Babylon. Yet Hezekiah's doctors had tried everything, he knew. Still—he wrinkled his brow. In the depths of his memory something stirred. He remembered vaguely hearing Obed talk of a poultice of figs. If only he were here now! Isaiah smiled as he thought of how he had wrapped Shear-jashub's cut finger in a fig leaf and how it had stopped the blood almost at once. Yes, he would go back and suggest it. It could do no harm. As he retraced his steps to the palace, the voice of the Lord came to him and Isaiah rejoiced at His words.

Isaiah hastened into the King's chamber. "What do you want with me now?" Hezekiah said wearily.

"I have returned to tell you that the Lord, the God of

David thy father, has heard thy prayer. He has seen thy tears, and behold, he will add unto thy days fifteen years."

Hezekiah lifted his hand weakly and pushed Isaiah away. "Go," he said. "Now it's you who come to me with false hopes."

"No, no, it's true," Isaiah said, kneeling at the King's bedside. "And there is more to delight your heart. The Lord will deliver the city out of the hand of the King of Assyria and will defend it from harm."

"Why should I believe your words any more than I should place faith in the sugared words of these others about me?" Hezekiah breathed heavily. "I have made my peace. Now let me be. I know *I am deprived of the residue of my years. I shall not see the Lord, even the Lord in the land of the living; I shall behold man no more with the inhabitants of the world. My habitation is plucked up and carried away from me as a shepherd's tent.* I have rolled up my life like a weaver."

"No, no," Isaiah insisted, his tears starting again. "The Lord is ready to save you. Listen to me." But Hezekiah turned his face away. "The Lord will send a sign that He will do this thing that He has spoken," Isaiah added.

"You say the Lord will send me a sign?" Hezekiah sat up in bed, straight and firm, for the first time in many days.

Isaiah nodded. "But first I want your doctors to make a cake of figs and lay it for a plaster upon your boil, and then you shall recover."

"It will be done at once," Hezekiah said. "Now what is the sign of the Lord?" He glanced out the window, the sun gleaming on the sundial in the courtyard. "How soon will I be able to go out in the sun again?"

"Keep your eyes on the sundial," Isaiah said. "Mark it

well. Behold the Lord will cause the shadow of the dial, which is going down on the sundial of Ahaz, to return backward ten degrees."

"Backward?" Levi gasped, marveling. "That would be a wonder indeed."

Even as Hezekiah gazed at the sundial, the sun returned ten degrees.

Hezekiah fell back on his bed. "Isaiah, my friend, my guide, my very own heartbeat, let us rejoice in the words of the Lord. *We will sing songs to the stringed instruments, all the days of our life in the house of the Lord.* Be always by my side for you are dearer to me now than ever."

But the closeness between Isaiah and Hezekiah did not last. After he had recovered, Merodachbaladan sent a delegation to Hezekiah with a magnificent present *"for he heard that he had been sick."* Hezekiah, flattered by the representatives from Babylon, proudly *"showed them his treasure-house, the silver, and the gold, and the spices, and the precious oil, and all the houses of his armour, and all that was found in his treasures; there was nothing in his house, nor in all his dominion, that Hezekiah showed them not."*

When word of this reached Isaiah, he grew furious. He went to the palace at once. Hezekiah received him immediately. "I thought you might be too busy to see me," Isaiah said. "It seems that you are entertaining visitors from abroad."

"Yes," Hezekiah said, greatly pleased with himself. "I want you to meet these Babylonians. They have brought me—"

"They have brought you blindness and stupidity," Isaiah burst out. "How could you have been duped by them?"

"What do you mean?" Hezekiah was stunned. "It's an

insult to talk to your King in this fashion. These men have come here honorably, seeking our help. It would be flattering to us to be allied with such a great kingdom."

"Don't you realize that one moment, they are your friends, and the next, they are your enemies. You are nothing but a pawn in their own game of political ambitions. Don't you understand that by showing them our strength, you have also showed them our weaknesses?"

"I trust these men," Hezekiah said. "I depend on you greatly, Isaiah, but for the good of the country I can't be swayed by the judgment of one man."

Anger surged through Isaiah so that the words tumbled from his mouth like the roar of a waterfall. *"Hear the words of the Lord of Hosts: Behold, the days come, that all that is in thy house, and that which thy fathers have laid up in store until this day, shall be carried to Babylon; nothing shall be left, saith the Lord. And of thy sons that shall issue from thee, whom thou shalt beget, shall they take away; and they shall be officers in the palace of the king of Babylon."*

The King stood up, his hands trembling with rage. "Isaiah, you try my friendship too much. You can't frighten me with these threats. I'm not a child. Perhaps it would be best for you to devote yourself to teaching children their letters instead of trying to teach a king how to run his country."

Isaiah was stunned. He returned to his home, agonized in spirit. This time he realized he had provoked the King too far. He found Maher-shalal-hash-baz at home and he poured out his concern over the outcome of his disastrous conference with the King.

But Maher-shalal-hash-baz offered him no sympathy. "I've told you that I think you're wrong in advising Hezekiah to keep Judah all alone. I'm all for joining with Babylon and fighting Assyria."

Isaiah recoiled from his son's words. He stumbled out of the house into the gathering dusk. "There is no peace in my soul. No peace in my own home." But more than peace for himself, Isaiah wanted peace for Judah. "But who will listen?" he cried out in his agony. "How much longer will my voice be drowned out like a lost child crying in the market place."

All of a sudden, renewed strength filled his body. If the people in the palace would not listen to him, perhaps he could make the people in the market place listen.

"I cannot wait to cry out, *fallen, fallen is Babylon, and all the graven images of her gods are broken unto the ground.*"

But as Isaiah approached, he noticed much excitement in the market place. A weary group of travelers had just come in fleeing from northern Israel. Sargon was the new King of Assyria and he had taken up the reins of war where Shalmaneser left off. Northern Israel was now reeling under the might of Assyria's forces.

"Babylon and Egypt will be next," Isaiah said, but there was no one to hear.

Isaiah stood aside as merchants and beggars and children hurried past him, driven by curiosity. He, too, was curious but he bided his time.

He looked at the narrow booths bulging with their wares. A stall close at hand had sheepskin garments from Ramah, not many miles away, and next to it were displayed silks and spices from Arabia—who knew how many miles away? He reached out and touched the sheepskin cloak, and for a fleeting moment he thought of Noam and longed for the life of the Rechabites. But he knew there was no turning back.

If only there was someone he could talk to now. Someone who would put out a friendly hand and—.

He felt a gentle pat on his back and turned. "No, it can't be." He rubbed his eyes with his fist. "The sun has blinded me."

"It's not the sun." Obed put out his hand. "Your aunt and I have miraculously escaped," Obed said. "Israel is nothing but a handful of dust now. Sargon has taken more than 20,000 of my people captive and is scattering them like seed in the lands of his kingdom."

"Yes, it will be just as I feared," Isaiah sighed. "But where is Reba?"

"She's well, but exhausted. She is resting nearby. If it had not been for an old soldier, who remembered me and who I once helped when he was ill, we, too, would have been taken captive."

"Come, I'll help you with your things," Isaiah said.

"There's nothing to help us with," Obed said. "We have nothing. Wait, I'm wrong. We have a young man, who also escaped with us. If it had not been for his young strength, we might not have made it. But Jerusalem is his home and he drove us on with his will and desire to come back home and see if he could find his mother."

A tall young man approached them just then. "See, here he is," Obed said. "Your ears must have heard me talking about you and brought you here."

"I've been making inquiries about my mother."

Obed laughed. "The impatience of youth. If anyone can help you, Isaiah can."

The young man turned to Isaiah and there was something about him that seemed familiar. The shape of the face. The color of the eyes.

"Is your name Benjamin?" Isaiah asked.

"Yes, didn't Obed tell you?"

"No," Obed said surprised. "I didn't mention your name. What is it, Isaiah? You look so strange."

"Are you the son of Sarah, widow of Jonathan?" Isaiah continued.

"Yes, yes," the young man cried out. "You know my mother. Where is she? What—"

"You will find all the answers to your questions at my home," Isaiah smiled.

And so Isaiah turned from the affairs of state to the affairs of his family.

Day by day the men and women of Jerusalem
watched a steady stream of camels . . .

Chapter 9/

Isaiah could not shut out news of the world or events at the palace. Maher-shalal-hash-baz and Shear-jashub reported to him that officials and wealthy men of prominence from Egypt, as well as Babylon, were seeking Hezekiah out and urging him to join them against Assyria.

Isaiah could not bring himself to go to the palace, but one morning when he heard that Hezekiah was on his way to the Temple to make a sacrifice, Isaiah decided to meet him there, hoping that the Temple background itself would make Hezekiah more willing to listen to God's words than to men's.

Isaiah waited until Hezekiah and his entourage were coming down the Temple stairs; then he stepped forward and greeted him warmly.

"I have missed you," Hezekiah said blandly. "But I know that you have much to keep you busy—your writing, your teaching—but don't let me stop you from making your sacrifice."

Isaiah stretched out his empty hands. "I came to make no sacrifice unless it is *Ariel, the city where David encamped.*"

A few stragglers on the Temple steps moved closer.

"Ah, Ariel, Ariel, the city where David encamped!
Add ye year to year, Let the feast come round!
Then will I distress Ariel,
And there shall be mourning and moaning;
And she shall be unto Me as a hearth of God."

The sound of Isaiah's voice attracted a steadily growing crowd.

"What does the Prophet say?" a man in the back called out.

"He calls Jerusalem *Ariel.*"

"What does he mean by *Ariel?* This is a strange word."

"Pay closer heed, my friend. Didn't you hear him call Jerusalem God's hearth? He says that David gave Jerusalem to God. Since this is so, and Jerusalem is God's home, then will he not spare us?"

"Quiet, you two," another voice shouted. "The Prophet speaks again."

"And I will encamp against thee round about," Isaiah said, fastening his gaze on Hezekiah.

"And will lay siege against thee with a mound,
And I will raise siege works against thee."

Hezekiah stirred uneasily. "Are you warning us that in a year or two, as one feast is passed by another, that Jerusalem will be in grave danger?"

Isaiah nodded. "Jerusalem shall be brought to the ground. Her speech shall be low out of the dust and her voice shall be as of a ghost out of the ground." His black eyes held Hezekiah as if hypnotized. "Do you think that God will thus abandon Jerusalem?"

Hezekiah wavered. "Do you think that I would be here if I did not believe in the faith of my fathers? Of course, I believe that God will protect us."

Isaiah stretched out his hand. "More than protect. *The multitude of thy foes shall be like small dust, and the multitude of the terrible ones as chaff that passeth away; Yea, it shall be at an instant suddenly—There shall be a visitation from the Lord of Hosts with thunder, and with earthquake—and a great noise, with whirlwind and tempest, and the flame of a devouring fire.*"

"Hallelujah!" the crowd burst out.

"*And the multitude of all the nations that war against Ariel,*" Isaiah continued, his voice rising and resounding above the excited shouts,

"Even all that war against her, and the bulwarks about
her, and they that distress her,
Shall be as a dream, a vision of the night.
And it shall be as when a hungry man dreameth, and,
behold, he eateth,
But he awaketh, and his soul is empty;
Or as when a thirsty man dreameth, and, behold, he
drinketh,
But he awaketh, and, behold, he is faint, and his soul
hath appetite—
So shall the multitude of all the nations be,
That fight against Mount Zion."

"That is good," Hezekiah said, pleased by Isaiah's words of assurance. "But must we wait for Jerusalem to be humbled in the dust? Isn't it better for us to use the strength of our arms in combating the danger that is near?"

"God is always near. Place your faith in Him. You need have no fear."

"Isaiah, I have always valued your advice, as you know. I would like to talk with you at length, but some worthy ambassadors have just arrived from Egypt. It's urgent that I see them immediately." Hezekiah's voice became soft and gentle. "I'm giving a banquet this evening for the ambassadors. Come with your sons. Hear with your own ears how foolish you are in your persistence. These men come from a great power, laden with dazzling wealth. Think what a privilege it would be for us to be allied with Egypt."

Isaiah sighed. Egypt. Babylon. They are one and the same, Isaiah thought sadly, but he agreed to attend. That night at the feast, Isaiah listened patiently as the Egyptians urged the creation of an alliance to break the power of Assyria. The time is opportune, they argued. Assyria was having difficulties elsewhere. If the Mediterranean nations would unite, Assyria could be humbled and tributes would cease. Isaiah shuddered as he heard the satisfied murmurs of approval sweep round the table. He was so astounded that he gagged and could not eat when he heard Eliakim stand up and urge Hezekiah to join with Egypt.

Isaiah could hold himself back no more. He sprang to his feet. "Hezekiah, I say *in sitting still and rest shall ye be saved, in quietness and in confidence shall be your strength.*"

Silence descended on the guests and all heads turned towards Isaiah. "*Woe to them that go down to Egypt for help,
And rely on horses,
And trust in chariots, because they are many,
And in horsemen, because they are exceeding mighty;*

But they look not unto the Holy One of Israel,
Neither seek the Lord!"

Maher-shalal-hash-baz plucked at his father's arm.
"Watch what you say, Father, or you will anger Hezekiah."

Isaiah brushed his hand off as if it were a fly. *"The Egyp-
tians are men, and not God,*
And their horses flesh, and not spirit;
So when the Lord shall stretch out His hand,
Both he that helpeth shall stumble,
and he that is helped shall fall,
And they all shall perish together."

"What do you really know about Egypt?" Shebna said.

"What do I know about *the land of the buzzing of wings,*
Which is beyond the rivers of Ethiopia;
That sendeth ambassadors by the sea,
Even in vessels of papyrus upon the waters!" Isaiah said.
"I know what the Lord has said to me:
I will hold Me still, and I will look
on in My dwelling place,
Like clear heat in sunshine,
Like a cloud of dew in the heat of harvest."

Isaiah picked up a piece of bread that lay untasted in his
plate. *"For before the harvest, when the blossom is over,*
And the bud becometh a ripening grape,
He will cut off the sprigs with pruning-hooks,
And the shoots will He take away and lop off." He pulled
a jeweled dagger out of the folds of his cloak and slashed
the bread in two, dropping it back into his plate.

"They shall be left together unto the ravenous birds of the
mountains,
And to the beasts of the earth;

And the ravenous birds shall summer upon them,
And all the beasts of the earth shall winter upon them."
He swept his huge hand across his plate and sent the bread crumbs scattering to the marble floor.

Shebna cut in again, his voice scornful. "That's good poetry," he laughed, "but is it good sense?"

"Is it good sense to rely upon a country where *they shall fight every one against his brother, and every one against his neighbor, city against city, and kingdom against kingdom.*"

The ambassadors from Egypt exchanged startled glances. "If I may interrupt," one of them said politely, "I object to your insinuations. You intimate that Egypt is on the brink of a civil war."

Isaiah faced the man directly. "Isn't it?" he challenged. "Isn't it true that your country is split in half by its loyalties? How many do you know who don't recognize Tirhakah's right to the throne? How many are there, within the palace itself, who are submitting to him unwillingly, and temporarily?"

The man seemed flustered for a moment. "You have no proof," he fumbled. "There are always dissatisfactions in every kingdom."

Isaiah held up his hand. "The proof is in your face and in your words." Isaiah turned to face Hezekiah. "How can you place our nation's destiny in the hands of a ruler whose own fate is so shaky? Pharaoh has usurped the throne and holds it only by a slender thread, the thread of tyranny and fear."

Both Egyptian ministers were now on their feet. "How dare you talk about our Pharaoh in this manner?" one of the men shouted. The other leaped forward, tearing Isaiah's cloak but Shear-jashub stood up quickly and intervened. Isaiah waved Shear-jashub aside. He faced the man, his eyes glowing. "I'm not afraid to say that

> *The princes of Zoan are utter fools;*
> *The wisest counsellors of Pharaoh are a senseless counsel;*
> *Where are they, then, thy wise men?*
> *They have caused Egypt to go astray.*

And now you wish to lead Judah astray."

A hubbub cut across the room and excited voices rose on all sides.

"No more," Hezekiah shouted across the table. "Silence, Isaiah. I will not have you insult officials from abroad! Leave at once!"

As Isaiah turned to go, Shear-jashub and Maher-shalal-hash-baz each took a place at his side. As they passed before the King, Maher-shalal-hash-baz stopped and bowed. "Hezekiah, my King, my friend, let me plead with you."

Hezekiah waved him away impatiently. "It's no use. You heard your father. He's a stubborn man."

"I'm not pleading for my father, but for understanding. Too long have I been blind. I have been like a man shivering in the cold with a blazing fire nearby, and I have been afraid of the flames, not realizing that fire can warm as well as destroy. It's tragic enough for a son not to understand his father's heart and break his home in two, but think well, O King, what a great tragedy it will be for you not to understand a true patriot's heart, and break your country in half."

But the time for understanding and words was past. Now was the time for action.

Hezekiah was swept along in the tide. He joined an alliance with Egypt, the Philistine cities, Moah, Edom and other provinces. In 714 B.C.E. Azur, King of Ashdod, withheld his tribute from Assyria and the others in the league followed suit.

The gesture of defiance brought swift action. Sargon descended like a whirlwind upon the Philistine cities that had begun the rebellion.

Isaiah was distraught by the news that Ashdod had been conquered. The members of his household suffered along with him, since he refused to eat and drink and his nights were spent awake or in a semi-waking state, and he moaned and cried aloud.

"Unburden your soul to the King," Obed urged. "Alert him to the dangers."

"I could tell him that the ruin of Ashdod is a mirror in which he can see Judah reflected, but words are useless."

"He listened to you in the past," Reba said. "He will listen again."

"No," Isaiah cried out and he tore off his luxurious purple and red cloak. In anger he hurled his shoes from his feet. "I will put on sackcloth," he said, "and walk the streets barefoot so that all will know that this is the way it will be when the King of Assyria leads away the captives of Egypt. And the people will cry out when they see me, *Behold, such is our expectation, whither we fled for help to be delivered from the King of Assyria; and how shall we escape?*"

For three years, Isaiah walked like a slave, barefoot and in the rough garment of a captive, and although Hezekiah still listened, and perhaps longed to join those who conspired against Assyria, he kept Judah aloof from military commitments.

At last, Obed and Reba decided they had shared Isaiah's hospitality long enough, and they prepared to leave Jerusalem. "We will seek a quiet home for ourselves out in the desert, at one of the outposts. We will be your eyes and ears, Isaiah. Should Sargon decide to attack Jerusalem, I know the way he will come," Obed said. "I will try to alert you."

But in 705 B.C.E. Sargon fell in battle and his empire fell with him. Babylon saw a new chance to gain world power. Egypt girded for a fresh attack. Tyre and Sidon plotted rebellion. Sennacherib, the new Assyrian king, determined to show the members of the league that Assyria was as strong as ever. His armies swept down upon the Phoenician cities, pillaging and slaughtering with ruthless fury. By 701 B.C.E. Sennacherib had conquered Edom and Moab and blazed a path of destruction across Tyre and Sidon.

It was too late now to warn Hezekiah to use the examples of Assyrian atrocities as a mirror in which he could see Judah reflected.

By this time Hezekiah was as worried about the military progress of Sennacherib as Isaiah. He took immediate steps to fortify Jerusalem. Anticipating a long siege of the city, Hezekiah ordered a tunnel to be built from a spring outside Jerusalem to the Pool of Siloam. In this way, he hoped to protect the city's water supply. Since each day brought fresh reports of Sennacherib's relentless drive against the allied nations, Hezekiah had ordered two groups of laborers to work on the water supply project. They had started at opposite ends, hacking their way through solid limestone rock to make a conduit. If they could finish in time, the water of the spring Gihon in the exposed valley would be brought within the city.

All Jerusalem watched the progress of the workmen with alternating fear and hope. One morning Maher-shalal-hash-baz hurried to tell Isaiah the good news. In a few hours, the men who had been digging from opposite sides would break through. "It is said they now hear each other's pickaxes," he said excitedly. "Hezekiah has ordered a celebration for the workmen this afternoon. It's said he is going out to the Pool of Siloam this afternoon to congratulate the men himself." Maher-shalal-hash-baz shook his head. "It really is incredible what they have accomplished. I spoke to the foreman and he says that they have covered between them, from each end, 580 yards."

"This is a sight to see," Isaiah said. "I'll go with you this afternoon."

But Maher-shalal-hash-baz knew that Isaiah was not going to see the tunnel. He was going to see Hezekiah and when Isaiah approached Hezekiah and spoke to him, Maher-shalal-hash-baz was afraid of what his father would say. But he took heart when Isaiah said, "Do not fear Assyria, Hezekiah. *Thus saith the Lord, the God of Hosts: O My people that dwellest in Zion, be not afraid of Asshur, though he smite thee with the rod. Mine anger shall be to their destruction. And it shall come to pass in that day, that his burden shall depart from off thy shoulder, and his yoke from off thy neck.*"

Hezekiah brushed Isaiah aside. "Sennacherib is so near that we can smell the stench of the dead. Please don't bother me. I must do what I can to save Jerusalem."

Isaiah recalled how once before he had been set aside rudely in this fashion by Ahaz, and he started to speak again, but Eliakim came to his side and drew him away from the King.

"You mean well," Eliakim said kindly. "But you are not a military man. You have no idea how bad matters are."

"I know," Isaiah said.

"*He is come to Aiath,*

He is passed through Migron;
At Michmas he layeth up his baggage;
They are gone over the pass;
They have taken up their lodging at Geba;
Ramah trembleth;
Gibeath-shaul is fled."

"Then you do know how little of Judah remains in our hands," Eliakim said.

Isaiah nodded. "Obed and Reba were caught in the Assyrian whirlpool and swallowed up. Benjamin brought me news of their death."

"I'm sorry," Eliakim said. "I have not been in as close touch with you lately as I would have liked."

"It's all right," Isaiah said. "You have more important things to do."

A workman approached timidly. "Noble sir," he said, bowing to Isaiah. "My men and I would like to ask you a great favor." He wiped the sweat from his grime-streaked face with his roughened hand. "For six months we have struggled in darkness and dirt. Now at last our water supply is safe. Jerusalem is safe."

"Safe?" Isaiah cried out in despair. "The water supply can't make Jerusalem safe, only obedience to God and an understanding of the ways of God can save us. But," he patted the perspiration-soaked shoulder of the workman, "tell me what favor you want."

The man hesitated. "We were thinking perhaps that you could carve some words on a rock to honor this great event. If we should die, then at least the world will know what we did."

"I shall be glad to carve an inscription for you, near the mouth of the tunnel, that all who come in future years may know of your work, for he who works with his hands is blessed."

"I'll get you the tools," the workman said eagerly.

And so, painstakingly, Isaiah carved into a rock nearby the following inscription: "This is the boring through. This is the story of the boring through: whilst the miners lifted the pick each towards his fellow and whilst three cubits yet remained to be bored through, there was heard the voice of a man calling his fellow, for there was a split in the rock on the right hand and on the left hand. And on the day of the boring through the miners struck, each in the direction of his fellow, pick against pick. And the water started flowing from the source to the pool twelve hundred cubits. A hundred cubits was the height of the rock above the head of the miners."

And Jerusalem itself was like a rock. The city refused to surrender to Sennacherib. Finally, a truce was arranged. Sennacherib was eager to save his military strength for the coming battle against Egypt, and Hezekiah was eager to save the capital from destruction. Hezekiah sent "ambassadors to the King of Assyria saying: I have offended. Return from me: that which thou puttest upon me will I bear."

It was a truce that was dearly bought. Hezekiah lost much of his land. The palace and the Temple were stripped of jewels. The very treasure which he had so proudly displayed to the Babylonians a few years before, Hezekiah now meekly handed over to Sennacherib. He even "cut off the gold from the doors of the temple of the Lord and from the pillars."

Day by day the men and women of Jerusalem watched a steady stream of camels and asses pass through the city gates bearing the country's wealth to the King of Assyria.

One morning, Uriah awoke Isaiah at dawn. "What is it, Uriah? More bad news for Judah?" Isaiah asked.

"I can no longer perform my duties at the Temple," Uriah said. "I can't stand by and see the workmen stripping the gold from the doors of the Temple."

"I didn't think gold meant so much to you," Isaiah reprimanded.

"It's not the loss of the gold that raises a storm in me but the loss of our self-respect. What's going to happen to Jerusalem when Sennacherib decides he's ready to attack us? You know this peace is a fake. It will last as long as Sennacherib wants it, and then he will crush us."

"Uriah, do you call yourself a priest of the Temple? Assyria is nothing but an instrument in the hand of God. Sennacherib is not punishing Jerusalem but it is God who is sending the Assyrian and his might *against an ungodly nation.* It is God who is guiding the Assyrian's hand *to take the spoil, and to take the prey, and to tread* (the people) *down like the mire of the streets.*"

"Are we to be scourged then, like Damascus—and Samaria?" Uriah asked.

"Why not?" Isaiah replied angrily. "You know better than I that we are a kingdom of idols. Why shouldn't God do to Jerusalem and her idols what he did to Samaria and her graven images?"

"Isaiah, I'm an old man," Uriah said. "I came to you for hope. If God is using Assyria to punish us, will he not punish Assyria, too?"

Isaiah put out his hand. "You see well for an old man. Yes, *when the Lord hath performed His whole work upon Mount Zion and on Jerusalem,* then He *will punish the fruit of the arrogant heart of the king of Assyria.*

Should the axe boast itself against him that heweth therewith?

Should the saw magnify itself against him that moveth it?

As if a rod should move them that lift it up,

Or as if a staff should lift up him that is not wood."

Isaiah strode about the room with such a heavy tread that the earth shook beneath his feet. "Sennacherib may think that he is all-powerful, but only God has power over all men and all nations. We are all instruments in His hand and what happens is but what He wills."

"I feel better now," Uriah said. "I'll get back to the Temple before they miss me. I shall tell them that *through the voice of the Lord shall Asshur be dismayed.*"

"Tell the people one more word," Isaiah said. "Soon *shall this song be sung in the land of Judah:*

We have a strong city;

Walls and bulwarks doth He appoint for salavation.

Open ye the gates,

That the righteous nation that keepeth faithfulness may enter in.

Trust ye in the Lord for ever,

For the Lord is God, an everlasting Rock."

With these words ringing in his ears, Uriah left.

. . . and his eyes glowed with pride at his two
sons, flanking him on each side . . .

Chapter 10 /

Before the day was out, Isaiah had another important visitor. Eliakim brought the news that, despite the gold and silver Sennacherib had taken in tribute, he now insisted on the surrender of Jerusalem.

"I am a man of God. I know nothing of military strategy. How many times have you told me this?" Isaiah asked in anger, then added quietly, "What kind of advice do you seek from me now?"

"Hezekiah would like your help," Eliakim admitted. "He's too proud to ask for it directly, but perhaps—"

"You may assure the King of Judah that God will protect Jerusalem. Sennacherib does not sit easy in his camp at Lachish. The Egyptians are massing for an attack against him. Some Rechabite friends of mine have told me that the Egyptians are moving north with a great army. It seems certain now that a battle will take place at Eltekeh. Sennacherib is not going to have time to waste on a long siege of Jerusalem."

"What if Tirhakah, the Egyptian king, is defeated?" Eliakim asked.

"No matter what happens, the Lord of Hosts will protect Jerusalem," Isaiah said. *"He will deliver it as He protecteth it.*

He will rescue it as He passeth over. In that day every man shall cast away his idols of silver, and his idols of gold and Asshur shall fall with the sword, not of man, and the sword, not of men, shall devour him."

"I will tell Hezekiah," Eliakim said.

But when he returned, there was great excitement at the palace. Sennacherib had sent Rabshakeh, a prominent official with the Assyrian army, with a letter outlining terms of surrender. Rabshakeh had been accompanied by an impressive military escort and he was waiting "by the conduit of the upper pool in the highway of the fullers' field" for Hezekiah's answer.

The news of the Assyrian delegation spread through the city and panic gripped the people. Some drawn by curiosity gathered along the walls to see the ambassadors of the great Assyrian King, whose conquests had been so many and so mighty.

As soon as Eliakim returned to the palace, Hezekiah sent him, Shebna and Joah, the son of Asaph the recorder, to see what terms they could work out with Rabshakeh. He instructed them to hear all Rabshakeh had to say but he warned, "If he tempts your temper, if he prods your anger, don't answer back."

With all due ceremony, the palace officials approached

Rabshakeh. "Hezekiah bids us discuss the message you bear from your king," Eliakim said.

"The King of Assyria would like to know in whom you trust so greatly that you have dared to rebel against him?" Rabshakeh said. "Don't you realize how vain and foolish it is to hold out against us?" Rabshakeh looked up at the growing crowds on the walls of the city. He knew the tongues of many tribes and this gave him an idea. "Listen," he called to the onlookers, "you have put your trust in Egypt, which is a bruised reed, *whereon if a man lean, it will go into his hand, and pierce it; so is Pharaoh king of Egypt to all that trust on him."*

Eliakim stepped forward. "It's not our trust in Egypt that gives us our strength. We trust in the Lord our God."

Rabshakeh laughed aloud and his mocking voice carried to the tops of the wall. *"Is not that He, whose high places and whose altars Hezekiah hath taken away?"*

"You don't understand our ways," Eliakim said. "The high altars were places of heathen worship and—"

"Well, then," Rabshakeh taunted, "tell me of the great strength of your soldiers. I'll make you a wager. My master, the King of Assyria, will give you two thousand horses, if you can find riders for them. What fools you are to depend on Egypt for chariots and horsemen. And as for your God, do you think I have come up without the Lord against your land? No, the Lord said to me: Go up against this land and destroy it."

Shebna pulled Eliakim and Joah aside. "We can't allow him to speak this way. The people are fearful enough. He will only unsettle them more. We must ask him to speak in another tongue."

"Right," Eliakim and Joah agreed. "I'll ask him," Eliakim

said. "Speak, I pray thee, unto thy servants in the Aramaean language, for we understand it," Eliakim pleaded, "and speak not to us in the Jews' language, in the ears of the people that are on the wall."

But Rabshakeh, realizing the power of his words on the throng said, *"Hath my master sent me to thy master, and to thee, to speak these words? Hath he not sent me to the men that sit upon the wall?"* Then Rabshakeh cried with a loud voice in the Jews' language, and said: *"Hear ye the words of the great king, the king of Assyria. Thus saith the king: Let not Hezekiah beguile you, for he will not be able to deliver you; neither let Hezekiah make you trust in the Lord, saying: The Lord will surely deliver us; this city shall not be given into the hand of the king of Assyria."* There were shouts from the crowd, but Rabshakeh's voice rose above the din. *"Hearken not to Hezekiah; for thus saith the king of Assyria: Make your peace with me, and come out to me."*

"This is not good," Eliakim said. "The crowd is growing restless. We must stop him."

"You can't do that," Joah said. "We must hear him out."

"Beware lest Hezekiah persuade you," Rabshakeh went on, *"saying: The Lord will deliver us. Hath any of the gods of the nations delivered his land out of the hand of the king of Assyria? Have they delivered Samaria out of my hand? Who are they among all the gods of these countries, that have delivered their country out of my hand, that the Lord should deliver Jerusalem out of my hand?"*

"This is blasphemy!" Eliakim cried out. "We can't allow him to say more."

"Remember Hezekiah said we mustn't provoke him," Joah said. "Let's hold our peace."

And they rent their clothes in their sorrow and went to Hezekiah and told him the words of Rabshakeh.

When Hezekiah heard the report, *he rent his clothes and covered himself with sackcloth.* "I will go to the House of the Lord to pray for guidance," he said. "In the meantime, Eliakim and Shebna, I want you to go with the elders of the priests, to Isaiah, and tell him, *'This day is a day of trouble. It may be the Lord thy God will hear the words of Rabshakeh, whom the king of Assyria his master hath sent to taunt the living God, and will rebuke the words which the Lord thy God hath heard; wherefore make prayer for the remnant that is left.'* Hurry, hurry," he urged. "I don't know where to turn now. Perhaps Isaiah can save us yet."

So the servants of King Hezekiah came to Isaiah. And Isaiah said unto them: "Thus shall ye say to your master: Thus saith the Lord: Be not afraid of the words that thou hast heard, wherewith the servants of the king of Assyria have blasphemed Me. Behold, I will put a spirit in him, and he shall hear a rumour, and shall return unto his own land; and I will cause him to fall by the sword in his own land."

Hezekiah was heartened when he heard Isaiah's words and he rejected the demands of the Assyrians, even though he knew that the Egyptians had been defeated at Eltekeh.

When Rabshakeh returned, he found that the King of Assyria had left the camp at Lachish. Tirhakah had rallied his forces again and was marching against the Assyrians.

In spite of this new danger, the King of Assyria confidently sent off a letter to Hezekiah saying: *"Let not thy God in whom thou trustest beguile thee, saying: Jerusalem shall not be given into the hand of the king of Assyria. Behold, thou hast heard what the kings of Assyria have done to all lands, by destroying them utterly; and shalt thou be delivered?"*

Hezekiah received the letter, read it, and *then went up unto the house of the Lord, and spread it before the Lord, saying:* "O Lord of Hosts, the God of Israel that sittest upon the cherubim, save us from his hand, that all the kingdoms of the earth may know that Thou art the Lord, even Thou only."

Isaiah then went to meet Hezekiah at the Temple. "*Thus saith the Lord, the God of Israel,*" Isaiah said. "*Since you have prayed to Me against Sennacherib, king of Assyria, this is the word which the Lord hath spoken concerning him: He shall not come unto this city, nor shoot an arrow there, neither shall he come before it with shield, nor cast a mound against it. By the way that he came, by the same shall he return, and he shall not come unto this city. For I will defend this city.*"

"I'll listen to you," Hezekiah said, "for if I do, *there shall be peace and truth in my days.*"

A strange plague broke out in the camp of the Assyrians: "*And the angel of the Lord went forth, and smote in the camp of the Assyrians a hundred and fourscore and five thousand. So Sennacherib departed, and returned* (to) *Nineveh.*"

After the Assyrians had been driven from their land, Hezekiah ordered a great feast that all might give thanks to the Lord, and do honor to Isaiah.

Isaiah's heart was filled with joy, and his eyes glowed with pride at his two sons, flanking him on each side, but his mind was churning with all the things that were yet to be done. He felt his age upon him and knew that there was much that he would have to leave undone. The more he thought of the years of trial ahead, the more his fears diluted his joy. Even at the banquet, the finest wine tasted sour to him and the meat unsalted, and he ate and drank little. Towards the end of the evening, the King turned to Isaiah and asked him to speak:

Slowly, Isaiah rose. "May all our days be filled with feasting. May our days be blessed with universal peace so that we may worship God, the one God of all nations, justly and righteously." He paused. "For many days I have been inflamed with a verse, the lines cutting like lashes into my brain. Let me unburden myself of it."

A hush descended on the hall. The cupbearers stepped back. The servants put the platters down and retreated to the walls.

"*And there shall come forth a shoot out of the stock of Jesse,*" the Prophet began.

"*And a twig shall grow forth out of his roots.*
And the spirit of the Lord shall rest upon him,
The spirit of wisdom and understanding,
The spirit of counsel and might,
The spirit of knowledge and of the fear of the Lord."

There was a clatter in the distant kitchen and a servant called out impatiently, "Hush, Isaiah speaks."

"*And his delight shall be in the fear of the Lord,*" Isaiah went on.

"*And he shall not judge after the sight of his eyes,*
Neither decide after the hearing of his ears;
But with righteousness shall he judge the poor."

"As you have done, Isaiah," Hezekiah cut in, "and as you have shown me to do."

Disconcerted, Isaiah rubbed his chin, trying to recall the continuity of the lines.

"*But with righteousness shall he judge the poor,*" he repeated,

"*And decide with equity for the meek of the land;*
And he shall smite the land with the rod of his mouth,
And with the breath of his lips shall he slay the wicked."

"Amen," cried out a ringing voice.

"*And righteousness shall be the girdle of his loins*," Isaiah went on smoothly and strongly.

"*And faithfulness the girdle of his reins.*
And the wolf shall dwell with the lamb,
And the leopard shall lie down with the kid;
And the calf and the young lion and the fatling together;
And a little child shall lead them."
Isaiah paused for breath.

"*And the cow and the bear shall feed;*
Their young ones shall lie down together;
And the lion shall eat straw like the ox.
And the sucking child shall play on the hole of the asp,
And the weaned child shall put his hand on the basilisk's
     den.
They shall not hurt nor destroy
In all My holy mountain;
For the earth shall be full of the knowledge of the Lord,"
Isaiah's voice rolled out like a throbbing drum, "*As the waters cover the sea.*"

The long speech wearied Isaiah. He excused himself and left. When he reached home, he collapsed.

Shear-jashub and Maher-shalal-hash-baz helped him into bed. As he lay back, Isaiah felt his life ebbing from him. He had done what he could and God had been good to allow him to see the fruits of his labors. He called his two sons to his side. "It's time now for you and the chosen among you to go forth as the remnant of our people and to make the voice of God the loudest in the land. Let His voice resound above the din of battle; above the barter of the market place. Keep His voice ever fresh and green in the land."

"We will follow in the path you have set us," his sons promised.

"Be assured," Isaiah said, "that the Lord will recover the remnant of His people that shall remain from Assyria, and from Egypt, and from the islands of the sea. He will assemble the dispersed of Israel, and gather together the scattered of Judah from the four corners of the earth." And he whose voice had been like a tempest in the night was now like the soughing of a spring breeze.

When Hezekiah heard that Isaiah was nearing the end of his days, the King came to him, his face unashamedly wet with tears. He knelt at Isaiah's bedside and Isaiah's two sons made way for him. "Once you came and knelt at my bedside," Hezekiah said, his head bowed. "Once you came and gave me hope. If only I could come to you and give you the years that the Lord has added to my life."

Isaiah smiled wanly. For the moment, he could not summon the strength to speak.

Hezekiah clasped Isaiah's limp hand in his own. "Take comfort and strength from what I say. *Good is the word of the Lord which thou hast spoken.*"

Isaiah lifted himself with a mighty effort. "*Behold, God is my salvation. I will trust and not be afraid, for God the Lord is my strength and song.*"

Then his voice died out and his head fell back.

When the King saw that Isaiah would speak no more, he left his side and cried aloud, "There lies a man the likes of whom the world will never see again."

Hezekiah spoke true. In the generation upon generation that has been born since, never has the world seen another man to compare with Isaiah.

It would be wonderful if we could end our story of Isaiah now but legend claims that he survived a few more years and lived to see the ascension of Manasseh, Hezekiah's son. Manasseh was the opposite of his father. He liked luxury and easy living. His followers did not approve of Isaiah. It is written of Manasseh that "he shed innocent blood very much, till he had filled Jerusalem with it from one end to the other." It is said that Isaiah was "sawn asunder." This seems to mean that in some way Isaiah was savagely murdered. And so to the name of Isaiah—prophet, poet, statesman—we add martyr. But this badge of glory is not needed in order to keep the memory of Isaiah and his love of God alive through the centuries. For Isaiah was a modern prophet. The things he worked for are still to be. Peace. International understanding. True democracy. Belief in one God for all. Today in the twentieth century, we, too, cry out as Isaiah did in the eighth century: "Lord, how long?"